JUST
ONE LAST NIGHT…

For Olwyn Deane and Lillias Jensen—
two wonderful women who have enriched the
fabric of my life since the day I was born.

Amy Andrews has always loved writing, and still can't quite believe that she gets to do it for a living. Creating wonderful heroines and gorgeous heroes and telling their stories is an amazing way to pass the day. Sometimes they don't always act as she'd like them to—but then neither do her kids, so she's kind of used to it. Amy lives in the very beautiful Samford Valley, with her husband and aforementioned children, along with six brown chooks and two black dogs. She loves to hear from her readers. Drop her a line at www.amyandrews.com.au

Recent titles by the same author:

RESCUED BY THE DREAMY DOC
VALENTINO'S BABY BOMBSHELL
ALESSANDRO AND THE CHEERY NANNY

JUST
ONE LAST NIGHT…

BY
AMY ANDREWS

First published in Great Britain 2011
by Mills & Boon, an imprint of Harlequin (UK) Limited,
Eton House, 18-24 Paradise Road, Richmond, Surrey TW9 1SR

© Amy Andrews 2011

ISBN: 978 0 263 21907 4

Harlequin (UK) policy is to use papers that are natural, renewable
and recyclable products and made from wood grown in sustainable
forests. The logging and manufacturing process conform to the
legal environmental regulations of the country of origin.

Printed and bound in Great Britain
by CPI Antony Rowe, Chippenham, Wiltshire

CHAPTER ONE

DR GRACE PERRY hated feeling unprepared. She'd happily lived her entire adult life totally prepared for all situations. She liked being prepared. Loved it, actually. It gave her power and a sense of control.

She loved control.

And order. And predictability.

Otherwise there was just chaos. And Grace hated chaos.

Unfortunately there'd been precious little order and too much chaos in the last eighteen months.

So today she planned to take back control.

All she had to do was get the job.

An interview she was feeling totally *unprepared* for after her early-morning flight from Brisbane and Tash's door slamming condemnation from last night still ringing in her ears.

Grace sighed as she pushed the lift button. How could a sullen fifteen-year-old girl have defeated her—broken her—so utterly? Taken her nice, neat, ordered, *controlled* world and turned it totally on its ear.

Grace hated defeat.

The lift arrived and Grace put the rare moment of self-pity aside as she strode into it and pushed the button for the eighth floor.

Such negative thoughts did not bode well going into the interview of her life. And however hard it had been on her to become guardian to her niece and nephew, it had been a thousand times worse for Tash and Benji.

The doors opened at her destination and Grace took a moment to straighten the dark grey skirt that flared around her knees, balancing out the flare of very feminine hips. She did up the large buttons on her matching jacket.

You can do this, she lectured herself as her strappy pumps sank into plush carpet. You are a fantastic emergency physician with fifteen years' experience and a respected manager.

You are outstandingly qualified.

Opposite the lifts was a large reception desk and she made her way to it.

'Dr Grace Perry to see Dr John Wilkie,' she said, injecting a note of calm assurance as if the interview was no more trifling than a sutured finger or a strep throat.

The starched-looking receptionist peered at her over half-moon glasses and frowned. She consulted her watch and then some paperwork. 'You're early.'

Grace blinked, feeling as if she'd committed some horrible transgression. 'Yes. It's a terrible habit of mine.'

Or it used to be anyway before chaos had taken over.

'Sorry,' she added, feeling the need to apologise to the un-amused woman in front of her. Then she smiled to reassure the receptionist it wouldn't happen again and to vanquish the horrible feeling of being caught on the back foot.

The receptionist sniffed then stood. 'Please follow me.'

Grace did as she was instructed—she didn't dare not to—following the woman's brisk march through a series of corridors until they reached a door and entered a lounge area.

'Take a seat. Dr Wilkie's conducting another interview.' She sniffed again. 'He may be a while.'

'That's fine,' Grace murmured, sinking into the nearest lounge chair. 'I have some work to do,' she said, patting her bag.

The receptionist departed and Grace was left to her own devices. Self-directed as ever and rather than think about who was on the other side of the closed door opposite, making a play for *her* job, she hauled out her laptop, placing it on the low table in front of her. She adjusted her glasses and waited for it to power up.

Twenty minutes later she was fully engrossed in a report when her mobile rang. Distracted, Grace searched through her bag for it. Normally she'd have it attached to her waistband but she had this bloody impractical skirt on today instead of her regulation trousers with their convenient loops so she'd thrown it in her bag.

It trilled insistently as Grace pulled out the entire contents of her bag onto the table in an effort to locate it.

Where could one little phone hide, for crying out loud?

She finally located it and pushed the answer button. 'Dr Perry,' she said.

'Hello, Dr Perry, this is Juanita from Brisbane City High.'

Grace gripped the phone harder as a surge of dread rose like a monster from the deep inside her. 'What's she done now?' She sighed.

'Natasha hasn't shown up today. Again. That's the third time this week.'

Grace shut her eyes. 'I see.' She knew her niece had been dropped at school. There'd been a text from Jo, the nanny, when she'd disembarked in Melbourne that morning, telling her so.

'Right, thanks. I'll deal with it.'

Grace's hand shook as she tried Tash's mobile. It went to the message bank and Grace left a terse message. She rang Jo next and informed her, then texted her niece.

Get your butt to school. Now!

Grace wasn't overly worried about Tash. If her niece ran true to form, she'd be at the local shopping centre.

Hopefully not shoplifting this time.

Grace was pretty sure Tash had learned her lesson from her brief foray into petty crime. But that boy would probably be there too. What was his name? Hayden? Jayden? Braydon? Something like that... And that was cause for concern.

Caught up in the drama as she was and the sick feeling that had been fermenting in her gut for eighteen months, Grace startled when the door opened abruptly and two male voices intruded on her disquiet.

'Thanks John, I look forward to hearing from you.'

'No worries, Brent. The successful applicant will be informed by the end of next week.'

The hairs on the back of Grace's neck prickled and it had nothing to do with the way the two men shook hands, slapped backs and generally interacted like the outcome was a foregone conclusion.

And everything to do with Dr Brent Cartwright.

Her first love.

She rose abruptly to her feet as if she'd been zapped by some sort of divine cattle prod. Shock waves buffeted her body as twenty years fell away in an instant and the memories flooded back.

His deep, rich voice. The rumble in his laugh. The way he'd looked at her like she was the only woman on the planet. How he'd enjoyed teasing her. The way he'd told stories. His generosity. His intellect. His attention to detail.

The heat of his mouth.

The smell of his neck.

The way he'd filled her more perfectly than any man ever had.

The way he'd shaken his head, his angry words when she'd broken their brief engagement. Broken his heart.

Broken both their hearts.

'Ah, Dr Perry,' John Wilkie greeted her from the door. 'Edwina said you were here already. Give us a few minutes, would you?' he requested as he backed through the door and shut it again.

Grace nodded dumbly, her pulse tap-dancing a frantic beat at her temples, but had eyes only for an equally stunned-looking Brent.

Brent stared. He couldn't help it.

Grace Perry.

The one that got away.

He was momentarily speechless. Twenty years and yet the memories rushed out at him. Walking hand and hand through the uni campus as the leaves had changed and they'd fallen in love. Skipping classes. Staying in bed for days in a row. Talking endlessly into the night. Eating cold leftover pizza for breakfast too many mornings to count.

Drinking cheap cafeteria coffee as they swatted up for anatomy exams, desperately trying to catch up on the things they'd missed.

She'd been his first love.

He took a step towards her, reached out a hand. He felt as gauche as a schoolboy. As unsure as the eighteen-year-old man who had considered her way out of his league but had wanted her anyway.

He finally found his voice. 'Gracie...'

She stiffened as his endearment yanked her back to the present. 'It's Grace,' she said, taking a step back. 'Just Grace.'

Brent stilled as her don't-touch-me vibe sparked other memories. The cold stab of her *it's-over* speech. The hard bite of the solitaire engagement ring she'd curled into his palm. The straightness of her spine as she'd turned away from him.

He stuffed his hands into his pockets, embarrassed by the impulse and surprised how, even after all these years, it was automatic for him to reach for her.

But if she could be cool and collected, so could he. 'How are you?' he asked politely. 'You're interviewing for the head of emergency?'

Grace nodded. 'You too?'

'Yes. I've been acting in it for the last four months.'

His voice flowed over her like warm butterscotch sauce oozing into long-forgotten places and Grace's heart banged like a bongo in her chest. It had no right to betray her. It should be sinking in her chest, not thumping merrily along like it wasn't aware of the implications of Brent's words.

What hope in hell did she have of getting the job if there was already someone acting in it?

She groped around for another subject. 'Have you stayed in Melbourne all these years?'

Brent nodded, keeping his face neutral. 'Some of us don't consider that a hardship, Grace.'

It had been twenty years but the slight clench of his jaw still gave him away. *She'd pissed him off.* She raised her chin and forced herself to shrug.

'It wasn't meant to be a criticism.'

Brent, oh, so familiar with that little chin lift, regarded her for a moment. She'd changed. And yet she hadn't. Her hair was shorter. Her hips were even curvier. She wore trendy glasses instead of contacts. And fashionable clothes. Her make-up had been artfully applied.

But her grey eyes still looked at him the same steady way they always had. The same old frankness was there. And her full lips still parted softly the way they always had, as if silently begging to be kissed.

Her lip gloss was the same too, he noticed absently. It still glistened like dew on cobwebs and its heady vanilla essence curled delicious fingers around his gut. He didn't have to try it to know it would still taste like honey.

But he wanted to.

He wondered how many years apart it would take to erase that tantalising aroma from his memory cells. The one that occasionally drifted elusively through his dreams.

Brent stared at her mouth for what seemed an age and Grace felt heat build everywhere as she ruthlessly suppressed the nervous—or was that wanton?—urge to trace the outline of her lips with her tongue.

But even more dangerous to her equilibrium was the storm surge of emotions welling inside her. Feelings she'd long since buried spluttered to the surface. The sense of rightness and belonging he'd always stirred inside her. The feeling of completeness when he'd held her.

All of which she'd rejected twenty years ago.

Maybe emotions like that were just too strong to ever truly forget?

She shook her head, fighting to wrest back control.

This was crazy.
Certifiable!
It had to stop...

And then the door behind Brent opened abruptly and John Wilkie was smiling and calling her in, before disappearing back into the room.

'Coming,' she said, dragging her gaze from the searing heat of Brent's.

She turned back to her bag, the contents still strewn over the table, stuffing it all back in, shutting her laptop lid and shoving it in too. Aware of Brent's heavy stare the entire time—feeling it in her breasts and her belly and her thighs.

But mostly in her heart.

Items slipped through her useless fingers, dropped to the floor, rolled out of reach. Grace wanted to weep she felt so clumsy and...

Out of control.

Chaos reigned again.

Damn it!

She forced the last item in and stood, taking a couple of deep, calm breaths. This interview was important. And she was the best one for the job. She needed to be composed. Prepared. In control.

She drew in three more cleansing breaths before turning to face Brent again. 'It was...nice...seeing you again,' she said politely, before gathering all her bravado and walking past him, her head high.

And her knickers twisted into the mother of all knots!

Nice? Nice! Brent stared after her until the softly shut door completely obscured her.

Nice?

It had been surprising. Shocking. Startling.

Cataclysmic.

He sat down on the nearby lounge and shook his head.

Nice? Damn, it was *anything* but *nice*.

Even now his body was stuck back in first-year uni, skipping class to stay in bed with her all day. It was a wonder the two of them hadn't contracted a vitamin D deficiency. Or turned into vampires.

They'd certainly had insatiable appetites!

Brent absently rubbed his jaw as the memories played like an old film reel in his head. He'd never quite managed to erase the images of her. Not through twenty years of distance or even two impulsive marriages and their subsequent fallouts.

And here she was. At Melbourne Central Hospital.

Déjà vu.

Confounding him again. Making him feel things again. Challenging all his assumptions about her being firmly in his past.

He dropped his head in his hands and shut his eyes. For some reason he'd been so sure they'd never cross paths ever again. Her goodbye had been so final—he'd never doubted she meant it even when he'd wasted two years harbouring secret fantasies about a reconciliation.

Meeting her today had been a huge jolt.

And very far from nice.

Dear God. What if she got the job? *His job.* What if he had to see her every day? Hear that laugh he'd loved so much. Watch that sway to her hips.

Smell that damn lip gloss?

Brent opened his eyes on a silent groan, his gaze falling on an object near his foot. He reached for it, realising it was a photograph. Grace must have dropped it from her bag when she was stuffing everything back in.

He stared at the image for a long time, trying to comprehend what he saw. Two children, a boy and a girl. The girl looked about twelve. The boy four, maybe five. Brother and sister?

They were laughing at the camera, their arms slung around each other's necks. Trees and a clothesline could just be seen in the background. They looked happy and loved.

And remarkably like Grace.

The girl more so. They both had her grey eyes but the girl had long blonde hair that fell in a white-blonde curtain to her waist, just as Grace's had back when he'd first known her. The boy looked more like Grace around the mouth. He laughed like her.

Grace had children.

His brain tried to reject the notion but he knew it somewhere deep in his gut. Just like he'd known all those years ago that she'd meant it when she'd said she was never coming back.

Grace had children.

Was she married also? Had she been wearing a ring?

A storm of emotions built inside him and he gripped the corners of the photograph hard. What the hell had happened to remaining childless? To *never, ever*?

That's what she'd said the day she'd given him back his ring. The day she'd received her second-year anatomy results and discovered she'd failed the subject. The day she'd totally flipped out, blaming them—blaming him—for derailing her career.

'I'm the eldest of ten children, Brent. I've lived in chaos and clutter and noise all my life. I've fed and changed and bathed and rocked and carted and carried and kissed skinned knees and babysat my entire life. And they're my family and I love them but I don't want that for me and I never want to do it ever again.

Never, ever.

I'm done with it all. I want to go far away. Live and work and experience somewhere else. Somewhere different. I want to be totally selfish for the rest of my life. To not have anyone but me to worry about. I'm going to make a great aunty—the best—but no babies for me.'

Brent stared at the picture—she'd lied.

Grace felt confident as she shook John Wilkie's hand half an hour later. Facing a panel interview was always nerve-racking and with the fates conspiring to knock her totally off balance before she'd even begun, she could have easily messed it up.

But she'd clicked into doctor mode, treating the interview like a multi-trauma case, drawing on the focus for which she was known. And she'd nailed it.

The get-the-job plan was looking up.

The last thing she expected when she exited the room was to find Brent waiting for her.

He gave her a rather grim look and stood. Grace's breath caught in her throat as he unfolded himself. She'd forgotten how he redefined the whole tall, dark and handsome thing. How broad his shoulders were. How his hazel eyes looked tawny in some lights. How his cleanly shaven jaw was impossibly smooth.

'How did it go?'

Grace blinked at the terseness of his tone. He seemed annoyed with her and she felt her hackles rise. Just because he was already in the damn job it didn't mean it was his. She really didn't have enough time or room in her life for his male ego.

'I nailed it,' she said bluntly.

Brent snorted. Of course she had. Grace had always done everything well. Failure was not acceptable to her—he'd learned that the hard way.

He passed the photo that had been eating a hole in his gut back to her. 'You dropped this.'

Grace frowned and took it. Her expression softened as she realised what it was. Tash and Benji. Back before their world had been turned upside down. Before Benji had cried himself to sleep every other night. Before Tash had dyed her hair black and pierced her nose.

They'd been so innocent.

She looked back at Brent, who was looking at her expectantly. Like she owed him some kind of explanation. And suddenly his terseness made sense.

It wasn't about the job at all.

She lifted her chin. 'Thank you.'

Brent scrunched his fingers into fists by his sides to prevent himself from reaching out and shaking her. 'You have kids.'

It wasn't a question and Grace hesitated for less than a second. She did. She did have kids. She may not have given birth to them, she may not have a clue how to deal with them, but they were blood and they'd been living under her roof for eighteen months.

And she loved them.

So, yes, she had kids. 'Yes.'

Brent nodded, shoving his fists into his pockets. Part of him had been hoping she'd deny it. 'You're married.'

Again, not a question. 'No.'

Brent rejected the slither of hope her denial engendered. 'Divorced?'

'No.'

'Widowed?'

'No.'

'In any kind of a relationship with their father?'

'No.'

Brent regarded her for a moment. She looked so aloof behind her glasses and her salon-styled hair. It was all layered and shaggy at the back with multi hues of blonde and brown. Her bangs swept across her forehead and the sides neatly tucked behind the ears. She looked like a poster girl in an optometrist's window.

Gorgeous but untouchable.

'In any kind of relationship at all?'

Grace raised her chin. None of this was his business and she was damned if she was going to unload the whole sorry story on him just because once upon a time he'd been a really good listener. Even if she did feel absurdly like doing just that.

The details of her personal life were on a need-to-know basis only. And he *did not* need to know.

'I hardly see that as being relevant, do you?'

So that was a no...'I thought you *never, ever* wanted kids.'

Grace did not appreciate his accusatory tone. 'I was twenty years old, Brent.' *God, had she ever been that young?*

He nodded. 'I do believe I made that point at the time but you were pretty adamant.'

Grace was weary. She spent most of her days arguing with a recalcitrant teenager. She didn't have the emotional energy to play one-upmanship with an ex-lover.

Even if he'd been her first.

And the best.

She shrugged. 'It was two decades ago, Brent. So sue me.'

Right now suing her was the last thing on his mind. Shaking her, on the other hand, was looking more and more viable. Putting her over his knee and spanking her even more so.

But there was a tiredness to her words, to the set of her shoulders that gave him pause.

She was right.

It had been twenty years. An age ago. They'd been kids. Young and in love and foolish.

And it belonged in the past.

He sighed. 'Would you like a tour of the department?'

Grace eyed him warily. The doctor in her was exceedingly interested in a tour of Melbourne Central's state-of-the-art Department of Emergency Medicine. She was, after all, hopefully about to become its director.

But the woman inside was urging her to run away. Fast. Do not pass go. Do not collect two hundred dollars.

Do not do anything that prolonged their time together.

Do not be foolish.

She'd been foolish with him before and where had it got her?

Flunking medical school.

She thought back to that day, that horrible day when she'd got her anatomy results. The fail had viciously yanked the blinkers from her eyes. Burst the happy little love-is-enough bubble she'd been floating around in.

She'd been on a scholarship, for crying out loud. With

twelve mouths to feed her parents hadn't been able to afford to send her to uni and she'd worked her butt off to earn that full scholarship.

One that had demanded academic success. Not failure.

She'd known right then it was medicine or Brent. Both of them were all-consuming. Both of them demanded a singular focus.

She'd had to choose.

She'd wanted to be a doctor since she'd been eight years old and had had her appendix out.

She'd loved Brent for two years.

And in those two short years he'd made her forget all her career aspirations and long-term goals. He'd made her fail anatomy. He'd put her scholarship on the line.

Ending it, transferring to another uni, had been the logical thing to do.

But it had hurt. Oh, how it had hurt.

Twenty years on the stakes were even higher. Her life was careening out of control and this was her chance to get it back on track. It wasn't just about her any more. There were two kids involved.

But how foolish would it be to pass up this opportunity? She needed to be informed and who better to do so than the current—if temporary—director? The doctor inside, the pragmatist, knew it made sense. And she'd got through the last twenty years, made a success of her life by listening to the doctor and not the woman.

It would be foolish to start doing so now.

CHAPTER TWO

BRENT put everything, including the fact that Grace was a rival for his job, aside and gave her the full tour. When he'd been seconded to Melbourne Central he'd been far from enthusiastic about the change. After fifteen years at the Royal Melbourne he had been utterly dedicated to his old hospital.

He'd planned on taking the helm, keeping the ship running until they found the right candidate and then head back to the Royal.

But since moving into the brand spanking new Melbourne Central he'd changed his mind. He'd realised he'd grown stagnant staying in one place. Roots were all well and good but the challenge of heading a new department, if only temporarily, had been exhilarating. And working with top-notch equipment in state-of-the-art facilities had been a luxury he'd quickly grown used to.

He'd put his stamp on this place and he was proud to share it with Grace. To show her that the boy with dreams she'd once known had more than fulfilled his goals.

He showed her around the twenty cubicles and seven resus beds, introduced her to the staff and demonstrated the central monitoring and fully integrated computer system that was run from the central work station.

Afterwards he took her around the other side of the station and opened a door. 'And this is my office.'

Grace looked inside. It wasn't palatial. But it was big enough, with a decent-sized desk and a very comfortable-looking leather chair. She looked at him. 'You mean my office?'

Brent gave a grudging half-laugh. 'Okay, the director's office.'

His laughter slipped over her skin like a satin nightgown—light and silky—and Grace smiled. For a moment. Before reality intruded. 'What will you do if I get the job?'

Brent regarded her for a few moments, wondering whether to tell the truth. He decided to give her no quarter. The old Grace hadn't liked to be mollycoddled.

'I hate to be the bearer of bad news but I really don't see that happening, Grace. I've been here since the beginning. They're only advertising the role because they have to. It's just a formality.'

Grace held his gaze. It was surprisingly gentle, considering the impact of his words, and had come over all tawny again. She appreciated his frankness. Hell, she'd suspected as much when he'd told her he was acting in the position.

Still, it irked. She needed it. Jobs like this at her senior level, with regular hours, didn't grow on trees. She wasn't just going to cede it to him.

'Well, we'll see about that, won't we?'

Brent saw the chin tilt again. 'You want it that badly?'

'I need it,' she corrected.

Brent knew the concession wouldn't have come easily to Grace and he saw in her gaze she was already regretting it. 'Need it?'

She hesitated for a moment, already cross with herself for giving away more than she should have and hyper-aware that they were standing very close in the small doorway. She could smell his aftershave wafting towards her and memories of how good it had felt to bury her face against his neck assailed her.

She took a step back, out of the doorway. 'More regular hours for the kids would be a blessing.'

Brent noted her withdrawal, pleased for the breathing space. It seemed twenty years hadn't dulled her effect on him. 'What are their names?'

'Tash…' Grace cleared her throat. 'Natasha and Benji.'

He nodded liking the way her voice softened as she said their names. She sounded like a mother and it called to something primitive inside him. After all, he'd once hoped she'd be the mother of his children.

Children she hadn't wanted.

'You could still come and work here you know, if this position doesn't come off. We're always looking for staff. You could have a job with flexible hours.'

Brent surprised himself with the invitation. But good hospitals needed good doctors. And he knew she wouldn't be being interviewed unless she was damn good. He wanted the best for the Central, for his department. Their history was immaterial.

He shrugged. 'The offer's there, anyway.'

Grace glanced at him, startled. That was a big call. And very generous. But it also had danger written all over it. Her life was complicated enough, without repeating past mistakes.

'Thanks,' she said, filing it in a mental bin. 'So...' she looked around '...is there a minor ops room somewhere?'

Brent stared at her for a moment longer then took the hint. 'This way.'

They walked to a corridor that ran along the back of the department with several more rooms evenly spaced along its length.

'That's X-Ray through there,' Brent said, pointing to the door at the far end of the corridor. 'This here...' he indicated, opening a door '...is for minor ops.'

Grace perused the layout and equipment before they moved on to several other rooms, including a storeroom, medication room and an examination room for eye patients housing an expensive specialised microscope.

'Dokator Brent!'

'Oh, hell,' Brent groaned at the raised female voice from nearby floated towards them. He looked behind him at the trail of black scuff marks his shoes had left on the polished linoleum floor.

'Dokator Brent!'

The heavily accented voice was closer this time, more insistent, and Grace looked at Brent, perplexed. 'Who is that?'

'That's Sophia,' he said, frantically scrubbing at the nearest mark with his shod foot. 'She's the department's cleaner. She's a dear old thing, has to be about ninety years old. Russian or Slavic or something like that. Salt of the earth but takes fanatical pride in her floors. Does not like having them besmirched, and these damn shoes always leave horrible marks.'

As Grace watched he moved on to the next black smudge. She stared at his shoes. They looked expensive—a far cry from the tatty sneakers he'd worn when they'd been young and in love.

'I don't usually wear them, except of course I had the interview today. She'll give me a terrible tongue lashing,' he groaned, the sole of his shoe erasing the marks.

Grace smiled. She couldn't help herself. Brent Cartwright terrified of a little old lady. She laughed then, unable to stop herself. Twenty years fell away and she was back at uni with him, goofing around.

He looked up at her laughing face and it took his breath away. She was looking at him like she had back then, like the intervening years had never happened. Like they were still lovers.

'Oh, you think it's funny?' He grinned at her, letting the years disappear. 'Just you wait. Trust me, no one wants to be on Sophia's bad side.'

She laughed again as he smiled and his foot scrubbed at the floor. Another 'I vill find you, Dokator Brent' came from very close by.

Brent stopped what he was doing, grabbed Grace by the hand. 'Quick,' he whispered, and pushed her through a nearby door, pulling it closed after them.

Grace didn't register the small confines of the room or the fact that it stank of the cleaning products that weighed down its three rows of shelves. It seemed to be a supply room. Not much bigger than a cupboard really. She was laughing too hard to even notice how close they were standing.

'Shh,' Brent whispered.

Just then the door opened abruptly, pushing them even closer together as they huddled behind it to stay obscured. He put his hand over Grace's mouth to help stifle her laughter. He felt the texture of her lip gloss as a waft of vanilla and honey drifted his way.

What was it called again? Honey something…

Sophia called out, 'I know you here somewhere, Dokator Brent.'

The door shut again but not before Grace heard Sophia muttering under her breath in some strange tongue.

Grace pulled his hand aside and burst out laughing again. 'Oh, God, I'm so sorry, Brent.' She grabbed his shirt as she leant forward a little, trying to catch her breath and laugh at the same time.

'You should see your face. I can't believe that the big important *Dokator* is afraid of a sweet little old lady.'

'She isn't so sweet when she's pointing a mop at you.'

He grinned down her. She was so…familiar, so…*Gracie* it was impossible not to.

Impossible also not to be aware that her hand was warm on his chest and her breasts kept grazing the front of his shirt as laughter spasmed through her rib cage. Or the vanilla aroma of her lips, which somehow overpowered the smell of bleach and hospital-grade disinfectant. Or that his hand was firmly planted on one of her hips and all he needed to do was exert minimum pressure and she'd be pushed against him completely.

Grace slowly became aware of his fading smile and his growing silence and the fact that she was scrunching his shirt in her hand. He felt tense beneath her grip and he was staring at her mouth. He was big and warm and so very near.

So very Brent.

She eased her hold on his shirt and absently smoothed it

with her palm. 'Sorry,' she muttered, as she became aware of the heavy thud of his heart beneath her fingers.

'I needed that,' she said, to ease the growing silence.

Today had been stressful, and this unexpected laughter had been the perfect release. Still, the fact remained that she was in a cupboard with Brent, giggling like a teenager.

It was insane.

She straightened slightly and put her hand on his chest, levering some distance between them.

'Pleased me and my shoes could be of assistance,' he said, moving back, as much as he was able in the confined area, placing temptation further out of reach.

Grace smiled at his joke. 'I think it's safe to go out now.' She checked her watch. 'And my plane leaves in a couple of hours.'

'That's a flying visit. Are you not even dropping in on your parents?'

Grace shook her head. She hadn't told her family. She didn't want to get anyone's hopes up. 'I saw them a couple of weeks ago,' she lied. 'I have to get home to the kids.'

There was Tash to deal with. And Benji hadn't coped well with changed plans since his parents' accident.

The kids. Brent still couldn't wrap his head around that one. 'Who's looking after them now?'

'The nanny.'

'Very suburban mum,' he murmured, as an incredible surge of something potent—jealousy, longing—clawed at his gut.

Grace felt the husky edge to his voice all the way to her toes. And all the places in between.

She straightened her clothes, finger-combed her hair, adjusted her glasses. 'I have to go.'

Brent nodded as he watched her reach for the doorknob. 'It was…nice…seeing you again, Grace,' he murmured. His chest bubbled with absurd laughter at the irony of his understatement.

Grace's hand stilled in mid-twist. 'Yes. You too.'

Then she opened the door and walked out without looking back.

'I hate you,' Natasha said as the plane touched down at Melbourne's Tullamarine airport six weeks later.

Grace sighed. 'Yes. I got that.'

They'd been over and over her decision to move them all back to Melbourne. She wasn't about to have the same conversation in front of a couple of hundred strangers.

'I love Jayden. He loves me. How could you rip us apart like this?'

Grace looked into Tash's tear-stained face. Her heavily kohled eyes, the same colour as her hair, looked raccoonlike as her mascara ran. The twinkle of a shiny stone chip in her niece's previously perfect nose winked cheerfully amidst all the teenage angst.

Somehow, it managed to look even more ridiculous.

Grace was sorely tempted to roll her eyes and tell her niece to stop being so melodramatic. That being in love at the grand old age of fifteen was absurd and, contrary to popular romantic myths, the world would not end.

Even though she'd been a scant few years older and had, in actual fact, felt exactly like the world was going to end when she'd walked away from the only man she'd ever loved.

But she just looked at Tash and said, 'If he truly loves you, he'll want the best for you. As do I. And this is the best thing for all of us right now.'

She wanted to say, Do you think I want this? Do you want to uproot myself and my career and sell my lovely house I slaved countless hours to pay off and leave my friends and a job that I love? Do you think it was my plan to upend my entire life to accommodate two orphans? So I could live with a pissed-off teenager and an emotionally fragile little boy?

Do you think I wanted my sister to die?

But she didn't.

'Look,' said Benji, sitting on his haunches in the window seat, his nose pressed to the glass, 'we're here, Tash. We're here.'

Natasha, mouth open and about to let loose what Grace felt was no doubt another embittered teenage diatribe, turned to her brother, scrubbing at her face and forcing a smile on her face. 'Yep, Benji.' She squeezed his hand. 'Grandma will be waiting for us and all the cousins.'

And in that instant Grace's heart melted. Behind all that horrible teenage surliness and you-don't-understand-me façade was a really great kid. Whose whole carefree existence had come to an end in a crash of twisted metal.

She sucked in a breath and reminded herself to be patient.

Grace felt unaccountably emotional as they walked up the sky bridge into the terminal to be greeted by her entire extended family. The Perry clan—her parents and eight siblings and assorted progeny—surged forward and Grace felt as if she'd come home.

After fleeing Melbourne twenty years ago she hadn't expected to feel such a strong sense of homecoming. She'd happily made her life away from it all. And it had been a very good life. One that she'd been more than a little reluctant to leave behind.

But the events of the last eighteen months had been climactic and Grace felt like she'd been slowly sinking in quicksand.

And it was now up to her neck.

It felt good to know her family were throwing her a lifeline.

'Welcome home, darling,' her mother said, wrapping her in a tea-rose hug. The scent of her childhood.

'Mum,' she said, hugging back, holding on tight.

Her mother had aged so much since Julie's death. For a woman with ten kids she'd always been remarkably spry. Full of energy and lust for life. Grace had constantly marvelled at how she did it—goodness, she herself was exhausted just trying to keep track of two!

But Trish Perry was greyer now, more pensive, less energetic. The sparkle in her eyes had been replaced by shadow. The spring in her step had disappeared completely.

And the same for her father. They were just…less.

Grace stood back to let her parents hug their grandchildren. A lump rose in her throat as a tear slid from behind her mother's closed lids. A spike of guilt lanced her. Had it been wrong for her to take the two most tangible connections to her sister so far away?

But Natasha had desperately wanted to get away from Melbourne. Sure, she'd made a song and dance about always having wanted to live in the Sunshine State but no one had bought that. They'd known that she had wanted to get far away from the memories.

And, in the end, they'd all agreed that it might be for the best.

How were any of them to know it had been an unmitigated disaster?

'Come on,' Trish said over the general din, wiping at the tear before disentangling herself, all mother-of-ten business-like again. 'Let's get you all home. I've made roast lamb, your favourite, Benj, and for you, young lady…' Trish ruffled Tash's hair '…I made chocolate crackles.'

Grace tensed and waited for Tash to primp her hair back into place or scoff at her grandmother's offering. The way she had when Grace had made a batch the week the kids had come to live with her—after a particularly harrowing night shift—because she'd known that they were her niece's favourite.

Tash's vehement *'You're not her'* had been cutting and Grace had been walking on eggshells ever since.

'Cool. My favourite,' Tash said.

Grace expelled a breath. *Teenagers!*

The next couple of weeks were crazy busy. Grace re-enrolled the kids in the school they'd been in prior to moving to Queensland—the school she herself had attended a million moons ago—and spent a small fortune on books and uniforms and all the assorted paraphernalia.

The school was local to the Perry family home, and was also attended by the current generation of Perry children. None of Grace's siblings had flown too far from the nest, all setting up house within a ten-kilometre radius of the family home and sending their kids to the same school they'd attended.

She had been the only black sheep.

With the kids settled, Grace went house-hunting. Her parents wanted her to continue to stay with them and she was happy to until she found somewhere else. But Grace had been independent for too long to move back home at the grand age of thirty-nine.

Her brothers and sisters may have been happy to stay close but Grace had always wanted more. And while she was grateful to have the amazing support of her family after doing the whole *mother* thing alone, she needed her space too.

Her parents' home was just too chaotic—even more so than it had been growing up—with thirty grandchildren from babies through to teenagers coming and going at all hours of the day and night.

Grace had missed the love and laughter but not the sheer noise of it all. She'd forgotten how loud and busy it always was. And how everyone was in everyone else's business.

That was something Grace hadn't missed.

In short, she needed privacy. A place that was quiet. Still. A place that was hers.

It had been tempting to look at real estate on the other side of the city, close to her new workplace. Had she moved back to Melbourne in different circumstances it would have been exactly what she would have done. Found a dinky little terraced cottage in the inner city close to cafés and shopping.

But the point of coming home was to be close to family. Was to have them as an extended support system. Multiple places the kids could go and stay when she invariably got stuck at work. Always someone to pick up the kids if she couldn't. Cousins to have sleepovers, share homework or catch a movie with. Aunts and uncles to spoil them and take them places and keep an eye on them. Grandparents to babysit.

No more nanny.

So Grace very sensibly looked only at houses for sale in the immediate vicinity of the school. The market was much more inflated in Melbourne and Grace was shocked at the prices. Luckily she'd made a good return on her investment with her place back in Brisbane and she calculated she could afford a three-bedroom house without going into a hideous amount of debt.

Julie and Doug had provided for the children's expenses in their wills but they'd been heavily in debt at the time of the accident so there hadn't been much money left. And what there was Grace hadn't wanted to touch. It belonged to Tash and Benji and she knew her sister would have wanted the money to be put towards the kids' university educations.

By the end of the second week she finally found what she was looking for. It was about a kilometre from the school in one direction and even less from her parents' in the other. It was a post-war, low-set brick with a small backyard. It needed a little TLC—the décor definitely needed modernising—but it was of sturdy construction and she could afford it.

Tash had stared aghast at the lurid shagpile carpet in the hallway and the childish wallpaper in her room the day Grace had taken them to visit their new home. She'd also been completely unimpressed that she was going to have to share a bathroom with everyone else.

Benji had been kinder, his interest lying only in the fact that due to the backyard a puppy might be in the offing. Grace had fobbed him off, promising to think about it for Christmas.

But maybe, Grace thought as she signed the contract, she and the kids could work at modernising it together? She could let them make over their rooms—involve them. Working part time would be very conducive to a DIY project.

She had to try and engage Tash somehow. She'd hoped her

niece would get over her resentment at being forced to move from Brisbane but it was just one more thing for Tash to hold against her. She was stubbornly recalcitrant where Grace was concerned. She was pleasant enough with everyone else but cut Grace no slack.

It broke Grace's heart. She'd always been Tash's favourite aunty. Cool Aunty Grace. Whenever Grace had come back for holidays Tash had been Grace's shadow. They'd chatted on the phone every few days since Tash had been old enough to speak.

But those days had long gone.

'Be patient,' her mother had said.

Except patience had never been a virtue she'd mastered.

She was losing Tash. And she couldn't bear it. But she just didn't know what to do. How to reach her. She was a fifteen-year-old girl who had lost her parents and shut herself off from the one person she'd once been closest to.

The one person who could help her the most.

And with all this weighing on her mind, Grace would have expected there to be no room for thoughts of Brent Cartwright.

But she'd been wrong.

It had been eight weeks since she'd seen him, since that awkward moment in the supply room, and tomorrow she had to face him again.

And every day after that.

A heavy feeling had been sitting like a lead lump in her stomach ever since she'd accepted the job. Nervousness. A sense of dread.

And that she could cope with.

It was the rather contrary bubble in her cells and the fizz in her blood that made her uneasy.

Very, very uneasy.

CHAPTER THREE

'ANXIOUS about today, darling?'

Anxious? Grace was so nervous she could barely pick up her cup of tea without it rattling against the saucer.

Why her mother was the only person on the planet not to have switched to mugs was a complete mystery.

She looked around at the expectant faces at the table. It had been nice to slip back into the family breakfast ritual but this morning she could have done with a little less companionship.

The kids were inhaling cereal like they'd never eaten before. Her father was reading the paper. Her brother Marshall had called in on his way to work to drop off his two kids and was currently eating his second breakfast of the day.

'No.' Grace shook her head and forced down the toast that her mother had insisted on making her.

The food was in imminent danger of regurgitation but at least it gave her something to think about other than Brent.

Chew. Chew. Chew. Swallow.

Chew. Chew. Chew. Swallow.

'You'll be fine once you get stuck in,' Marshall added.

'I have a five-day hospital orientation first. Boring stuff like fire lectures and workplace health and safety stuff, so I won't be getting stuck in until next week. But at least its nine to five.'

'I hate starting a new job.' Marshall shuddered.

Trish nodded. 'It's always hard starting over somewhere new.' She squeezed her daughter's hand. 'I know you're my oldest and you haven't been little for a very long time, but I'll still worry as if it was your first day at kindy. It's not easy walking into a place where you don't know a soul.'

Irritated by being babied and by their incessant need to talk about what was making her feel incredibly nervous, she blurted out, 'Brent works there.'

There was a moment of double-take around the table that would have been quite comical to an outsider. Her mother sucked in a very audible breath. Her father looked up from his paper. Marshall stopped chewing in mid-mouthful.

'Brent Cartwright?' her father said.

'You didn't mention that before,' her mother said.

'Wow. That's a blast from the past,' Marshall said.

Tash looked from one adult to the other. 'Who's Brent Cartwright?'

'Grace's old boyfriend,' Marshall said, reaching for his fourth slice of toast.

Grace glared at him and turned to Tash. 'He was someone I knew a long time ago. We went to med school together.'

'I didn't think you were still in touch with him?' Trish said.

'I'm not.' She shrugged with as much nonchalance as she could gather. 'I…bumped into him when I came down for the interview. He works at the Central.' Grace kept it deliberately vague.

'Well, how is he? What's he been doing with his life? Goodness…it's been, what…twenty years? Is he married? Does he have kids?'

Grace realised she couldn't answer any of the personal questions about him. She hadn't asked about his life and he hadn't volunteered.

Had be been wearing a ring?

The lump of lead sank a little deeper into the lining of her stomach at the prospect. Which was utterly ridiculous. Of course he'd be married by now. With a swag of kids to boot. It was all he'd ever wanted.

A family to call his own.

She shook her head. 'I don't know, we barely talked,' she said.

'Well, how'd he look?' Trish sighed and fluttered her hand against her chest. 'He was always such a handsome boy.'

Marshall gave a hoot and Grace shot him her very best I-used-to-change-your-nappies look as she stood. 'I guess he still looks okay,' she muttered, figuring she was probably about to be struck down dead and that would, at least, cure her horrible bout of nerves.

He'd looked incredible. Just like the old Brent but with a maturity that had taken his sexiness to a whole new level. 'Anyway, gotta go.'

She bustled around to the other side of the table and dropped a kiss each on Tash and Benji's heads. Benji gave her one of his sweet smiles but Tash fluffed her hair as if to erase it.

Grace ignored the pointed action. 'See you both about five-thirty,' she said, picking up her case and turning to go.

'You should invite him to dinner one night. It'd be lovely to see him again.'

Grace stopped in mid-stride. She looked at her mother, ever the hostess. 'Mmm…' she said noncommittally, ignoring Marshall's wink in her peripheral vision, and headed towards the front door.

That was *so* not going to happen.

As it played out it wasn't until lunch of her third day that she finally met up again with Brent. She was standing in line at the cafeteria when a familiar sense of him surrounded her. She didn't have to look to know he was near.

It had always been like that between the two of them.

'Grace.'

She gripped her tray as his quiet greeting brushed her neck and nestled into her bones as familiar to her, even after all these years, as her own marrow.

She didn't bother to turn and face him. 'Brent.'

'What are you having? They do a good Chicken Parmigiana.'

'The quiche.'

Brent frowned at the continued view of the back of her head. 'Let me guess. With chips drenched in vinegar?'

Grace smiled. 'Yes.'

The waitress interrupted them and Brent let her order.

'That's twelve dollars fifty, Doc.'

'Here,' Brent said, smiling at the middle-aged woman behind the counter, 'add up mine too and take them both out of this.'

Grace, who was handing over her card, froze and finally faced him. 'I pay my own way, Brent.'

A man would have to be deaf, blind and stupid not to pay heed to the ice in her tone and the chill in her gaze.

But somehow it just made him more determined.

He shrugged. 'For old times' sake.'

A surge of molten rage erupted in her chest so fast it took her breath. Hadn't he learned anything from the *old times*? He'd wanted to take care of her and all she'd wanted had been for him to realise she could take care of herself.

She hadn't needed a carer. She'd wanted a partner. An equal. Someone who didn't need the trappings of the traditional to be validated. But Brent, a product of a broken home and an even more broken foster-system, had craved the conventional.

He'd wanted roots. A wife, some kids, the whole white-picket-fence catastrophe. And she'd just wanted a career.

'No.'

She didn't mean it to come out as a growl but she suspected from the rounded eyes of the nurse standing behind Brent that it had. 'Put it away.'

Brent nodded and withdrew his money, cursing his stupidity under his breath. It had been the wrong thing to do and the wrong thing to say.

Why did he suddenly feel like a gangly eighteen-year-old around her? Trying to prove he was a suave urbane gentleman and not some gutter urchin who had been dragged through a system that had been underfunded and overstretched?

She hadn't treated him as if he'd been unworthy back then— why would she now?

Grace paid for her meal. 'We need to talk,' she said, before she stormed off to an unoccupied table as far away from the nearest lunchtime customers as possible.

Grace continued to fume as she watched Brent charm the woman at the register and then his unhurried stride towards her. He'd been in a suit that day of the interview, which had only hinted at the perfection she knew lay beneath. But today he was in trousers and a business shirt that left nothing to the imagination.

Was it possible that he was even broader twenty years on?

'I'm sorry,' he said as he placed his tray on the table and sank into a chair. 'It won't happen again. In fact, I think you should pay for me next time. I reckon I could set up a tab here and have them bill you at the end of each month. You could also pay for my parking if you like.'

Grace, who'd opened her mouth to launch into her how-dare-you diatribe, shut it again. He was grinning at her and it seemed like nothing had ever gone wrong between them. How many times had they sat in a cafeteria, eating some awful uni food and laughing at his silly jokes?

It seemed like yesterday.

She raised an eyebrow. 'Surely the director of emergency medicine gets his own car space?'

Brent grinned again. 'Yeah, you got me there. So, just my cafeteria bill, okay?'

Grace felt all the angst melt at his infectious smile. *Seemed like she was still a sucker for that mouth.*

The urge to reach out and stroke the rich-looking fabric of his shirt, as she once would have done, prowled inside her like a living, breathing beast. She forced herself to pick up her cutlery instead.

As they ate they chatted about her orientation and Grace also told him about the house she'd bought. Twenty minutes passed easily. He loved listening to her talk. Her voice was just the way he remembered—soothing and melodic.

In fact, so many things about her were the same. Familiar. Her great big smile. Her mannerisms.

But the way her eyes crinkled at the corners when she laughed was new. She'd obviously done it a lot and he was torn between being happy for her and annoyed that she'd obviously had a rich and full life without him.

Of course her hair was completely different. And then there were the glasses. He knew she was severely long-sighted and was essentially as blind as a bat without some kind of corrective device, but what had made her switch from contacts?

'So, why the glasses?' he asked as conversation dwindled.

Grace shrugged and adjusted them with sudden nervousness. This was moving into personal territory.

'I've had so many problems with contacts over the years. Glasses are simpler. And they're excellent splash protection. I can't tell you how many times I've copped an unexpected spray of blood in my face and they've saved my eyes every time.'

Brent nodded. Having had a couple of splash injuries over the years, he could relate to that.

He liked the glasses very much—they, along with the short, layered hairdo, took her to a whole new level of sexy. There was a maturity to her sex appeal now that pulled even more treacherously at his libido than it had when he'd been a teenager.

She seemed all schoolmarm, all touch-me-not.

Perversely, it had the opposite effect.

He swallowed his last mouthful and pushed his plate away, sinking back into his chair. 'Have you been avoiding me?'

Grace looked at him, startled for a moment, before forcing herself to calmly pick up her cup and take a sip of her tea. They'd definitely moved beyond hospital safe-lift policy and dreadful wallpaper.

'The boss of the emergency department has an ego, I see,' she said dryly.

Brent chuckled. 'Is that a yes?'

Grace fought the urge to shut her eyes as his laughter bathed her in testosterone. *No one chuckled quite like Brent.* 'It's been a busy few days—that's all.'

'If you say so.'

Grace ignored the jibe and watched as he picked up his coffee cup the way he always had. His long, strong fingers disregarded the convenience of the curved handle, preferring to encompass the whole cup.

No ring. 'You're not married.'

The statement slipped out unchecked. Not surprising since his marital status had weighed on her mind since her mother had put it there.

But not something she'd wanted him to know she'd been thinking about.

Brent looked at her for a moment before looking down at his bare left hand. 'No. Not now.'

Now? Oh. 'Divorced?'

Brent nodded. 'Twice.'

Grace blinked. 'Twice?'

He nodded. Marrying twice and failing at both wasn't a record he was proud of. 'In my early twenties.'

After Grace had walked away Brent had been determined never to date another career-woman. And while party girls had been fun and up for anything, the reality of married life with a poor medical student or an overworked, underpaid resident had soon lost its sparkle.

'They were both brief. My first one didn't see out a year. The second one didn't see two. Both of my exes have since happily remarried. One now lives in Hong Kong. The other in Darwin. They were both amicable.'

'Okay,' she said. Because frankly she didn't know what else to say. She certainly hadn't expected that.

Deep down she'd secretly thought he'd never find anyone to replace her. That what they'd had was a once-in-a-lifetime thing. She'd certainly never found another man who'd come close to measuring up to Brent.

Brent could see she was grappling with the news. 'I was looking for... I wanted...'

He stopped. He hadn't known what he'd wanted.

Grace. But not Grace.

She nodded. 'Yeah...I know.' He'd wanted connection. Family. Roots. The perfect white-picket life he'd never had. 'Any kids?'

Brent shook his head. Forty years old and the kids he'd always imagined he'd have hadn't panned out.

He'd never been short of partners. In fact, he'd earned quite the playboy rep. But the problem with dating party girls was that they were as reluctant to settle and have babies quickly as career-women were.

And after two divorces, the idea of the perfect family had taken a battering. He'd resigned himself to the fact that he just wasn't meant to be a father.

'I guess I never found the right person. It just hasn't happened.'

Maybe perfect only came along once? Maybe he'd been holding out for another Grace? Sitting opposite her, he suspected that it could possibly be true. The thought alarmed him and he opened his mouth to distract himself from it.

'I coach a football team, though. Made up of kids in the system. It's run by a Melbourne-based charity.' He smiled, thinking about his beloved Little Warriors. 'They range in age from five to twelve. They're a bit of a ragtag bunch, but they're keen and they love their Aussie rules.'

Grace watched as Brent's face softened, his sexy mouth moving into an easy smile. His admission didn't surprise her. His time in foster-care had given him deep insight into a fraught system. That he would be doing his bit to improve it all these years later was typical of the Brent she'd known.

And after remembering him with her siblings, it was easy to visualise him running around on a field, chasing after a bunch of kids, a whistle in his mouth, laughing.

'Every few weeks I hire a corporate box at the MCG and we all go and watch a game together.'

Grace whistled. That wouldn't be cheap. 'They're lucky to have you.'

Brent shook his head. 'I'm lucky. They're great kids.' He gave a half-smile. 'They keep me young.'

Grace wished she could say the same about her kids. Tash was single-handedly turning her grey. 'Sounds great,' she said, trying not to sound resentful. Coaching a bunch of kids who hero-worshipped you for a couple of hours was very different to parenting day in, day out. *Especially when you weren't wired that way.*

'Enough about me,' he said, looking directly at her. 'You never married?'

She shook her head. 'Nope.'

'Why?'

There was a certain amount of amazement in his voice and she laughed. 'Women do chose to stay single, Brent. It's not a crime. Especially in a field like medicine where the climb to the tóp is a long, hard slog. I made a choice to put my career first.'

And it hadn't even been difficult. Sure, there'd been relationships over the years but none of them had stimulated her like medicine. Or Brent. She'd always figured she'd had her shot at grand love and blown it.

And if sometimes, deep in the night, she'd craved a man's arms around her, dreamt about Brent, it was the price she'd paid. And she didn't have any regrets.

At least she hadn't until Brent had swept back into her life, reminding her of things that could have been.

'And yet you had children?'

Grace frowned. It took a second for her to understand what he was saying. He still thought Tash and Benji were hers…

'Ah. Actually…I have a confession to make.'

Brent raised an eyebrow. 'Oh?'

She took a deep breath, already dreading the way she knew

this conversation was going to go. Rehashing all the grief and opening all the wounds again. 'They're not mine. Tash and Benji. They're Julie's.'

'Julie? Your sister?' She nodded and he continued, a smile lighting his face. 'Do you remember that time she called us at three in the morning from that nightclub? She was underage and had drunk too many West Coast coolers and she was scared she was dying from alcohol poisoning?'

He laughed at the memory. 'What the hell she thought two green medical students could do I have no idea.'

Grace smiled the familiar ache in her chest roaring to life. She remembered it as if it was yesterday. Julie hadn't touched a drop of alcohol since that night.

They'd been so close. With only eleven months between them they'd been more like twins—inseparable. And when Grace had made the heart-wrenching break to Brisbane to finish her medical degree she'd missed her sister almost as much as she had Brent.

'She threw up for a day,' Grace murmured. 'I had to come up with that elaborate lie for Mum and Dad.'

Brent chuckled. So the kids were her sister's. It certainly made a lot more sense. The notion of Grace having kids had been completely foreign to him and he'd spent a lot of time in the last weeks trying to wrap his head around it.

But that didn't explain why she hadn't set him straight from the beginning. Had she wanted him to think they were hers as some kind of proof that she'd been fine without him?

'So…you let me believe they were your kids because…?'

Grace cleared her throat of the huge lump that had suddenly taken up residence. 'Because they are. Mine. That is. Julie and Doug were killed in a car accident eighteen months ago. I'm…' She drew in a shaky breath. 'I'm their legal guardian.'

Brent felt his gut twist at the huskily imparted news. He sat very still for a moment, watching Grace fight to stay contained, observing the thick mist of grief clouding her grey gaze.

'Oh, no, Gracie…' He reached for her across the table, his

hand squeezing her forearm. He knew how close they'd been. 'I'm so sorry.'

His touch and the way he said her name, like he could see deep inside her bruised heart with just one glance, nearly brought her undone and she snatched her arm back. She would not break down in front of Brent.

In a public cafeteria.

For God's sake, she hadn't seen him in two decades!

It was ridiculous.

And if she started to cry now, she didn't know if she could stop. And then he would haul her into his arms and the way she was feeling right now, she'd go willingly.

Absurdly, he'd been the one she'd secretly craved most after Julie's death. Having him so near now was dangerous. Her life was complicated. Chaotic.

There wasn't room for any more.

'Thank you,' she said stiffly, refusing to acknowledge the flash of emotion she saw in his hazel eyes at her rejection of his touch.

'What happened?'

Grace filled him in briefly on the accident. 'Doug died instantly,' she concluded. 'Julie was cut free but died shortly after arriving at the Royal.'

Brent frowned. 'I must have been on holidays when it happened.' He thought back. Yes, he had been. He'd gone skiing in France with friends. 'I wish I'd been there when she came in.'

Grace sucked in a husky breath. She wished he had too. It would have made it somehow easier to bear to know that Julie had had a familiar face with her that night. To know that maybe she might not have been so frightened.

It should have been her.

If she'd been there, maybe she could have saved her sister. Maybe Brent could have.

'Me too.'

Brent nodded. She was hugging herself now, so removed, so

shut down. It was clear she was hurting and it killed him. He'd do anything to take her pain from her. But she was as closed off, as forbidding as that day she'd told him she was leaving and excised him from her life.

And it hit him—any thoughts he'd been harbouring deep down that they might have a chance at rekindling their relationship were utter fancy.

She was no closer to committing now than she had been back then.

And he was no sadist. In the aftermath of their devastating break-up and two failed marriages he'd hardened his heart to relationships and happily settled into a life of playing the field.

After a childhood of being pushed from pillar to post, Brent knew all about loving the one you were with.

He wasn't about to lose his head to her a second time. She'd walked away last time. And he was damned if he was going to allow nostalgia open the door to her again.

'I wish I'd known,' he said, falling back on polite socially acceptable conversation. 'I know it's probably too late but is there anything I can do...'

Grace shook her head. 'You already have. I'm very thankful that you offered me this job when I didn't get yours. Not many places offer part-time work at my level and I really appreciate it.'

Grace had been devastated when she'd been informed she hadn't been successful. And had rejected Brent's job offer that had come soon after. But then Tash had gone AWOL after school a few days later, scaring the absolute daylights out of her, and as much as she knew it would be challenging for them to work together again, she'd known she needed to come home.

So she'd swallowed her pride and emailed him.

He shrugged. 'I want the Central's emergency department to be the best. It makes sense to hire the best.'

Grace paused, trying to decide whether to mention the elephant in the room or not. But she'd always believed in tackling things head on. 'I appreciate that it's not easy, given our history. I know it'll be awkward to start with.'

Brent nodded. Then he held out his hand. If they set the boundaries at the beginning, they'd both be on the same page. 'So let's make a pact. The past is the past. Today is a new page. Friends?'

Grace's heart thunked in her chest as her hand slid into his and his warmth flowed up her arm and through her body. 'Friends.'

Brent felt it too and quickly withdrew his hand. 'We kinda skipped that part, didn't we?'

Grace gave a half-smile. They certainly had.

She suddenly felt on steadier emotional ground. She looked at her watch. 'Gosh. I have to go.' She stood. 'Thank you. For... being so understanding.'

He shrugged. 'What are friends for?'

Grace smiled, picked up her tray and departed. Brent watched her walk away. The sway of her hips drew his gaze to their hourglass curve and her cute bottom and he had to remind himself of the pact he'd made just a few seconds before.

Friends.

CHAPTER FOUR

GRACE was pleased to get her first day in the actual department started. She loved emergency medicine and even a few weeks away from it had left her yearning for the hustle and bustle.

It was the sort of work that was completely absorbing, leaving no time to worry about anything in the outside world. And now she and Brent had agreed to be friends, there was no reason for apprehension.

It was actually a respite for Grace to come to work.

She'd been too free to over-think her situation over the last few weeks, and the problems with Tash and the uncertainty of what would happen next had been unsettling.

She never felt unsettled at work. At work there was certainty.

And control.

As she entered Melbourne Central's emergency department via the sliding doors fifteen minutes before her official start time of eight a.m., Grace pulled in a deep lungful of hospital air. The smell of antiseptic and floor polish was as familiar to her as her own minty toothpaste breath and she almost sighed out loud.

She wanted to stop in the middle of the all-but-deserted waiting area with its rows of hard plastic chairs and announce, 'Honey, I'm home.'

She smiled to herself as she kept walking, nodding to the nurse at the triage desk as she made her way to the empty staffroom. Stowing her bag in the locker she'd been allocated, she fixed herself a quick cup of coffee at the kitchenette and wandered out to the handover room where she knew the night medical staff would be passing on information to the day doctors.

The handover room, used by both medical and nursing staff, was an office off the main medical station that formed the central hub of the department. It wasn't very large and consisted of an overflowing desk, crammed bookshelves weighed down with medical texts and several chairs.

There were two large glass windows so comings and goings could be watched, and on one wall was a large fixed whiteboard with various patients' names and conditions corresponding with the cubicle number they currently occupied.

Grace introduced herself to the assembled residents and registrars. A large glass jar that sat on the desk containing assorted lollies was passed around and the handover began. Two minutes later Brent strode into the room.

'Sorry, I'm late,' he apologised. 'Bloody traffic is getting worse. Terrible impression to give the new kid on the block. Sorry, Grace, I know how you hate tardiness.'

Grace bristled as she felt the force of several speculative gazes. Yes, she did abhor tardiness. Growing up in a family of twelve, they'd rarely been on time anywhere, and punctuality was one of the things since flying the nest that she'd always prided herself on.

But the familiarity of his greeting, not to mention the way his damp hair curled around his collar and the distinct soap and aftershave aroma he'd brought into the room with him, rankled.

He'd filled the room with such effortless masculinity and, in the process, transported her back twenty years.

When what she really needed was to be in the here and now.

'I'll make sure HR docks it from your pay, Dr Cartwright,' she murmured.

It scored her a couple of laughs but also, she hoped, delivered her message loud and clear. Friendship had its limits.

Brent heard it loud and clear. Obviously being friends didn't entail anything too familiar.

Fine by him.

But still, as the report progressed he realised how hard it was going to be in reality to ignore their history. He was super-conscious of her. Of knowing that beneath her tailored trousers and cotton shirt lay very familiar territory.

He remembered what she looked like naked.

How she liked to be touched.

And what she sounded like when she came.

It may have been twenty years but those memories were still just as potent today. He'd forgotten nothing.

'So what time is the ultrasound booked for the suspected gall bladder?' Grace asked the night reg.

Brent, who hadn't realised he'd tuned out, dragged his mind out of Grace's underwear and tuned back in to the hand-over. Hopefully, seeing Grace regularly like this—at work, as colleagues, in a non-sexual way—would blunt those old memories.

Hopefully, they'd eventually dissipate altogether.

Hopefully.

It took all of Grace's willpower to block out Brent's presence in her peripheral vision but once she had, she found herself enjoying the relaxed atmosphere of the handover. Her new col-leagues stopped every now and then to have a joke or throw in an anecdote.

The department was in its early morning lull so there was no need to rush. Not every morning was like this so it was great to be able to take their time when they could.

Brent joined in with his own witty observations and Grace could see how respected he was. The junior doctors deferred to him and he was generous with his support and knowledge. But he also challenged them to think laterally and to look outside the box when answers were elusive.

And he was liberal with praise, murmuring, 'Good catch,' when an apparent case of heartburn at two in the morning had been correctly diagnosed as an impending myocardial infarction.

She also wasn't blind to the level of interest other than professional. Two of the female residents were looking at him like he'd been dipped in chocolate, all but smacking their lips, watching him from under half-closed eyelids. Had they been the ones clocking off she might have put it down to exhaustion but as they were only just starting their shift, Grace wasn't fooled.

He'd always been a chick magnet. Even when they'd been a hot and heavy item. Secure in his love for her, she'd found it amusing, often teasing him about it.

She wondered how many women had shared his bed since.

'All right, then, thanks, folks, go home,' he addressed the night staff. 'Get some sleep.' He stood and looked at the day shift. 'Let's get this day started.'

Grace blinked, surprised they were finished. The others also stood and started to file out of the room and she followed suit automatically, trying to erase images of Brent and bevies of faceless women.

'Grace, can I have a word, please?'

Grace paused and held back, waiting for the room to empty. She felt off balance, confused, and grappled to claw back control.

Brent reached for the jar of lollies and helped himself to one. He contemplated apologising for the over-familiarity earlier but decided to put it down to teething problems with this new relationship they were trying to forge.

'Just want to check you're all set for your first day. Were you happy with your department orientation last Friday? Sorry I wasn't here for it. Do you need me to go over anything else with you?'

Grace wasn't sorry at all if the last twenty minutes in his distracting company was any indication. 'I'm good,' she said.

'Raring to go, actually. I think I'm okay with everything, thanks. But I'll ask if I'm unsure.'

Brent nodded. Of course she was on top of things. Grace was always on top of things. 'I'm going to be in a meeting for most of the morning. Do you think you'll be okay? Sorry, I did want to be around for your first shift.'

Grace was relieved that he wasn't going to be around. She'd be too self-conscious anyway. And not just for personal reasons either. Professionally she had a lot to prove.

Even though they were at the same level, technically he was her boss and his opinion of her medical skills mattered to her. She tried to tell herself it was professional pride and it was, to a degree. But it went deeper than that.

They'd been med students together, weaving dreams of medical greatness. On a personal level, his approval also meant a lot.

Maybe even more.

'I'll be fine,' she confirmed. She'd rather get a feel for the place first before she had Brent scrutinising her every move. 'Don't worry about me. I promise not to kill anyone.'

Brent smiled. 'Good to know.'

'Right, well,' she said, glancing at the door and then back at him. 'I'll…see you around, then?'

Grace didn't wait for his acknowledgement. She turned on her heel and left the room.

The morning turned out to be fairly standard fare for an emergency department. An assortment of minor incidents and accidents—a broken arm, an asthma attack, a case of angina. And then the usual mishmash of things that should be seen in a GP clinic—sore throats, a case of the flu, an ingrown toenail.

It was perfect to allow Grace to ease into the routine. To get to know where things were, who was who and how to work things like the computer system and the different forms. Of course, she would have coped with being thrown in at the deep end too but slow and steady was preferable for her first shift.

The nurse manager for the department, Ellen, was lovely and obviously highly experienced, and even formally introduced her to the intimidating Sophia. The older woman gave her the once-over, paying particular attention to Grace's shoes.

'You wear good shoes,' she said. 'Leave no marks. Is good. We will get along.'

'Er…excellent,' Grace said, relieved to have passed the Sophia test.

'Don't mind her,' Ellen said as Sophia hobbled away. 'Her bark is worse than her bite. She'll do anything for you. Underneath all that bluster she's a real sweetheart.'

'Dr Perry? Ellen?'

They turned to find Barb, the triage nurse, approaching. 'The bat-phone just rang.' The nickname they gave to the phone that provided a direct link to the ambulance coms centre rolled easily off Barb's tongue.

'Stabbing at St Barney's high school. Seventeen-year-old male with knife wound to his central chest. Conscious, orientated, no visible signs of bleeding, obs stable, saturating at ninety-eight per cent. Eight minutes out.'

Ellen looked at Grace. 'Game on.'

Grace felt the familiar kick of adrenaline buzz through her system as they hustled to the resus area. She welcomed it. She knew it would sharpen her instincts, hone her responses, help her make the split-second decisions needed in situations such as these.

'A stabbing at school?' she said to Ellen as she rang the lab to activate the massive transfusion protocol.

'We get a lot of stabbings, not usually school kids, though. Melbourne's got a bit of a seedy underbelly and the inner city has quite a high crime rate. Gunshot victims, stabbings and other violent assaults are quite common.'

Grace nodded. She'd grown up here. Gangland killings had been part and parcel of Melbourne's street life throughout her formative years. But in Brisbane shootings and stabbings were the exception rather than the rule. Grace realised she was going to have to adjust her expectations.

'What's happening?' Brent asked, joining them in Resus. 'You paged me?'

'No.' Grace looked around. 'I didn't.'

'Sorry, I did,' Ellen said. 'This could get messy and I thought it would be better to have as many hands as possible.'

Grace read between the lines. Ellen didn't know her. Fair enough. The nurse couldn't know that Grace had spent a year in Chicago's busiest ER and could crack a chest open with her eyes closed.

A lot of doctors of her experience would have been annoyed and she could see Ellen bracing herself for consequences. But Grace knew the nurse manager was only being cautious and admired her for her initiative. Hopefully, after today all the nursing staff would have faith in her abilities.

'Sure, the more the merrier,' Grace confirmed.

Brent smiled at her, relieved Grace hadn't gone all prima donna on Ellen. A lot of his colleagues would have had their noses totally put out of joint by Ellen's presumption but Grace had taken it in her stride.

It was a good sign. He hadn't known until now what kind of a doctor she was. Sure, she had an impressive CV, but he'd never experienced her in the role, worked side by side with her as a doctor. Often what applicants looked like on paper bore no resemblance to what they were like in action.

In his experience a good doctor wasn't just clinically brilliant but was a team player. And one who didn't recognise that nursing staff were their partners in this crazy thing they did day after day was very shortsighted indeed.

And he was jazzed to be finally working with her. After all, this was what they'd dreamed about twenty years before. Living, loving, laughing, working together. And although the first three might not apply now, he was excited to be finally fulfilling the last.

Watching Dr Grace Perry in action was going to be a real treat.

They bustled around, donning yellow paper gowns and gloves, preparing drugs and instruments, alerting Theatre, readying chest tube and thoracotomy trays.

'You want airway or wound?' Brent asked as the distant wail of a siren punctuated the activity.

'Wound.' She didn't hesitate. She needed to prove herself today and that was the quickest way.

The siren got louder and they rushed outside to greet the ambulance. Brent reached for the back doors and opened them to reveal a paramedic doing chest compressions with bloodied gloves.

'He crashed about thirty seconds ago.'

The paramedic stayed on the trolley, giving a rapid-fire handover as he continued to administer CPR and they rushed the gurney into Resus. He jumped off as the team quickly transferred the critical teenager onto their trolley.

'Get the O-neg started, stat,' Grace said as she placed a stethoscope against the chest wall, working around Ellen who'd taken over compressions and another nurse who was hooking the patient up to the monitor.

'Size eight ETT,' Brent said to the nurse who was assisting him.

'Stop compressions,' someone said. Ellen stopped and they all looked at the monitor. V-fib.

Ellen recommenced as Brent announced, 'I'm in. Let's bag him.'

'I need to crack his chest,' Grace said, pulling the stethoscope out of her ears. The knife had obviously severed a major vessel in his chest or maybe even his heart, and they didn't have time to mess around.

'He's full of subcutaneous emphysema,' she said to the registrar opposite, 'Place a chest tube.'

'Let's give some adrenaline and atropine,' Brent ordered.

A nurse pushed an open pack towards her and held out a

pair of sterile gloves. Grace thrust one hand and then the other into them as if she'd been a surgeon for the last fifteen years.

'Thanks,' she said. 'Could you prep?'

Ellen stopped compressions as some iodine was squeezed over the chest.

'Still VF,' Brent said.

'One litre from the chest drain and rising,' the registrar announced, as blood flowed into the collection chamber.

'Come on, kid, do not die,' Grace said as she made a swift incision.

Her hand was rock steady and her focus laser sharp but somewhere at the back of her mind she realised she didn't even know his name. She was about to stick her hands in his chest and she didn't even know the most basic thing about him.

'What's his name?' she asked no on in particular.

'Dean.' The answer came from the back somewhere.

Dean. *Such an innocent-sounding name.* 'Retractor.'

A gloved Brent slapped it into her hand and she positioned it, cranking it slowly apart, watching as more and more of the chest cavity came into view. Blood welled up and poured from the wound. 'Suction!'

'Can you see it?' Brent asked, peering over her shoulder.

'Too much blood,' she muttered, running her gloved fingers over the surface of the fibrillating heart, going by feel alone. Her fingers slid into a groove. 'Yep, got it—must have pierced the right atrium.'

'Sutures?'

Grace nodded and he handed her a loaded needle. The operative field was clearer now the collected blood had been sucked away and she could visualise the rapidly oozing wound on the surface of the heart.

'Tell Theatre we'll be ready in ten,' she said to Ellen as she deftly placed some very rough sutures to close the defect. It wouldn't win her any needlecraft awards but it didn't need to be perfect—just effective. The surgeons could do the rest.

'Still in VF,' Brent murmured, and every set of eyes switched to the monitor.

'Internal defib,' Grace said. She squeezed Dean's heart between her two hands as Brent readied the paddles.

'Here,' he said, passing them to her. They looked remarkably like a pair of salad tongs or long-necked spoons. 'Charged to fifteen joules.'

Grace applied them to either side of Dean's heart muscle. 'Go.'

The small electric current charged through the heart. Grace did not remove the paddles as her eyes sought the monitor.

'Still V-fib.'

'Again,' Grace ordered. Come on, Dean! *What the hell are you kids doing, taking knives to school?*

The paddles were charged again. 'Go.' Everyone held their breath.

This time the frenetic green squiggle changed to a different rhythm. It was slow but essentially normal and Brent announced triumphantly, 'Sinus brady.'

Grace swore she heard the exhalation of a dozen collective breaths. They'd done their jobs, now it was up to the surgeons.

And to Dean.

He was by no means out of the woods.

Brent squeezed her shoulder. 'More adrenaline. More atropine. Hang more blood,' he said to the nurses working with the drugs and fluids. 'Let's get him to Theatre to finish the job.'

Ten minutes later Dean had been whisked off to the operating theatre by the surgical team, who had swarmed in like an efficient army of ants and taken over his care.

'Well done, team,' Brent said as they watched the rapid departure of Dean's trolley. 'Fantastic effort. Amazing result.'

The resus bed area looked as if a bomb had hit it. Grace's gown, along with several others, was covered in blood. They were all looking a little in shock. But it was insignificant at that moment.

Brent's words had given voice to their own thoughts. It *had* been amazing, Grace acknowledged as she rode an adrenaline high, allowing herself to recognise it for the first time.

By God, they'd done it! Pulled a seventeen-year-old boy back from the brink of death.

'Well done to Grace especially,' Ellen said, stripping off her gloves and gown. 'It's going to be a pleasure working with you, Dr Perry.'

Grace, also stripping off her bloodied garments, grinned at her co-workers as they all nodded in agreement.

She'd passed the test.

Grace was on a high for the rest of the shift. They'd heard from the surgeons that Dean had made it through his op and was in the ICU. He'd started to wake and they were feeling optimistic about his long-term prognosis.

Today was an excellent day.

It was so good she didn't want to go home and spoil the buzz. Why was it that she could stick her hands inside the chest of a human being and sew up a hole in a heart but she couldn't figure out how to deal with a fifteen-year-old girl?

Grace shook her head to dispel the insidious thought. For now she *was* at work and she'd ride the high while she could. There was time enough for downers later.

As the afternoon progressed Grace spent a lot of it dealing with Dean's case. As it was an attempted murder investigation there were protocols to follow and the paperwork was endless. She'd also been interviewed by three sets of different police.

Nothing like that for a buzz-kill.

An hour before her shift ended she was reviewing X-rays with Adam Mather, a resident, on a suspected bowel obstruction case, when she heard Brent's voice. She looked up and could just see him through a crack in a pulled curtain around a nearby cubicle. He was talking to a very anxious-looking man as he listened to the man's chest with a stethoscope.

Brent said something she couldn't make out and the man

laughed. The furrows in his forehead disappeared and his face cracked into a smile. Brent laughed also, taking the stethoscope out of his ears but leaving his hand on the man's shoulder.

So this was Brent the doctor.

A strange flutter vibrated through her rib cage. It was a revelation for her—this Brent. She'd never actually seen him in action as a fully qualified doctor. Not even this morning. She'd been too intent on what she'd had to do, on her own actions, to pay any heed to his.

Twenty years ago they'd spent a lot of time wondering what they'd be like as qualified doctors. Talked about it. Shared their hopes and aspirations. But she'd walked away from him after two years in medical school and had never seen the result.

She hadn't ever doubted he'd be good. Not just brilliant, compassionate too. Brent's earlier life had been full of harsh realities but instead of making him hard and bitter it had made him determined.

Determined to not treat people as numbers. To protect dignity and preserve self-respect.

Her heart swelled to see that he hadn't grown too big, too important to take a little time with an anxious patient. To crack a joke. To squeeze a shoulder.

A woman could love a man like that.

'Dr Perry?'

Grace blinked as Adam's voice intruded on her wandering thoughts.

Crazy thoughts!

Where the hell they'd come from she had no idea but they were *not* welcome. Last time she'd loved Brent it had smothered the life out of her.

And this time round there was no time for love at all.

CHAPTER FIVE

THE next two days in the department were comparatively uneventful—thank goodness. Grace had had a real baptism of fire and while she didn't mind a challenging case, where it was *go*, *go*, *go* with no time to think or breathe, she didn't want one every day either.

Okay, this was Melbourne, twice the population of Brisbane—she knew there'd be more. And she knew that she'd lose some. But Dean was doing well in ICU and she'd live on the glow of that success for as long as possible.

On this, her third day, she finally felt as if she was getting a handle on things like the layout and the forms and the different procedures. Her next run of shifts would help to cement that further but that wasn't until next week so she was concentrating hard today on consolidating what she'd already learned.

She couldn't quite wrap her head around working just three days a week. Brent had been very generous with her rostering. She would have to work an occasional weekend and do rare on-call cover, as did he, but essentially she was no longer a shift worker.

After fifteen years!

It was a big adjustment for her. But as hard as it was to be at home more, fighting her uphill battle with Tash, the extra days off did give her an opportunity to connect better with the kids. Grace just hoped that one day Tash would appreciate it. That one day she'd accept the hand that Grace kept holding out. And that Tash kept biting.

Grace was reviewing a CT scan on one of the desktops at the central station when she heard a familiar voice.

'If she's busy, don't bother her. I'll just tell her I was here when she gets home this afternoon.'

Mum? Grace stood. Yep. There was her mother standing at the triage desk, talking to Gabi. What on earth was she doing there?

Tash?

Grace almost groaned out loud. She checked her watch. There hadn't been a wagging incident since Tash had started at the new school. Trepidation squirmed through her belly as she shut down the screen and went to greet her mother.

'Mum? What are you doing here?'

Trish smiled at her daughter. 'Hello, darling.' She hugged Grace. 'Sorry, I hope you're not busy?'

Grace shook her head. 'Is everything okay? Is Tash okay?'

'Of course, everything's fine. I was just passing so I thought I'd drop in to see if Brent would like to come to the family barbecue on the weekend.'

Grace blinked. *Was she mad?*

'Er, Mum?' she said, pulling her by the arm out of earshot of Gabi, the lovely but gossipy triage nurse whose interest in all things Brent was borderline obsessive. She'd already filled Grace in on Brent's very active dating life.

'He's a very busy man, Mum, and besides...I really don't think Brent is interested in attending some family thing of ours.'

'Oh, but, darling, he used to love to hang out at home.'

Yes, he had. Brent had never been more at home than amidst the chaos of her noisy, crazy family.

She sighed. 'Mum that was twenty years ago. Brent—'

'Hello? Yes? Did I hear my name?'

Grace recognised Brent's powerful frame in her peripheral vision before she squeezed her eyes shut. *This could not be happening.*

'Brent!' Trish laughed as Brent swept her into a big hug.

'Mrs Perry. What a lovely surprise. How nice to see you again after all these years.'

'Oh, please.' She batted his chest. 'Call me Trish!'

Grace rolled her eyes. Was her mother *flirting*?

'What have you been up to? Grace tells me you're the director of emergency medicine here.'

Grace stood in agony for five minutes while Brent and her mother chatted away.

'Trish, I was so sorry to hear about Julie. Grace told me. It's just so tragic.'

For the first time since Trish had hugged Brent Grace saw her mother's smile slip. She gave him a pained smile, so sad it broke Grace's heart all over again. 'Yes, it is. We miss her a lot.'

Brent reached for Trish's hands, engulfed them in his own and squeezed. He'd been shocked to see how Grace's mother had aged. He laid the blame squarely on the grief blazing in the older woman's gaze.

'*C'est la vie*,' Trish murmured with a shrug, and cleared her throat of the emotion threatening to overwhelm her. 'Anyway, I was just saying to Grace, we're having a family barbecue his weekend and would love it if you could come along too. For old times' sake, you know? It'd be lovely to catch up with you.'

Brent was momentarily taken back. This he hadn't expected.

'I told Mum you were probably too busy.'

Brent flicked a glance at Grace. She looked like she'd rather have Ebola come to the barbecue. But then he glanced back at Trish and the misery in her eyes was his undoing. He couldn't bear to see anyone this sad.

'I would be delighted to attend.'

Trish grinned. 'Really?'

'Really.' He smiled back.

Trish clapped her hands and gave him a quick hug. 'Oh, that's great. Wait till I tell Lucas, he'll be so pleased. We often wonder about you. Won't it be great, darling?' she asked, turning to Grace.

Grace nodded. 'Peachy.'

Brent suppressed a smile at Grace's underwhelmed response. Luckily Trish seemed oblivious as she rattled off the details and then departed.

They stood in the waiting room and watched her go.

'I'm sorry. I realise that you'd rather I wasn't there. I just…' He looked down at her. 'She seems so sad. I didn't have the heart to say no. But I won't go if you don't want me to.'

Grace nodded, seeing the compassion and concern in his face reflected in the tawny shimmer of his hazel eyes. 'You can't back out now, Brent.'

'But you wish I hadn't said yes, right?'

He seemed suddenly intense and the heat smoking in his gaze travelled all the way down her spine and curled fingers deep inside. 'I don't think it's a good idea for us to see each other socially,' she prevaricated.

Brent's gaze dropped to her mouth. Her vanilla honey mouth. What was she afraid of? 'We said friends, right? Isn't that what friends do?'

Well, he had her there…except the way he was looking at her mouth didn't feel friendly. Neither did the rat-a-tat-tat of her heart.

Grace drew in a deep breath and took a conscious step back—how had they got so close? 'Of course,' she said with as much primness in her voice as she could muster. 'And the family would love to see you again.'

Brent became aware they were standing in the waiting area not far from the triage desk, with one very interested-looking Gabi and several waiting patients checking them out.

She was still capable of making him lose his head.

'Good, it's settled, then. Midday Sunday.'

'Midday Sunday,' she repeated.

High noon…

* * *

The doorbell chimed at precisely midday while Grace was halfway through chopping up a kilo of onions. She'd drawn the short straw, apparently because wearing glasses somehow protected the chopper from the fumes.

She dabbed at her inflamed eyes with a clean tea towel—*obviously not.*

She washed her hands under the tap, feeling her pulse rate kick up a notch. It had to be him—everyone else had arrived an hour ago. 'I'll get it,' she called out.

Brent was about to push the bell again when the door opened abruptly and a small 'Who are you?' drifted up to him.

Brent looked down over the top of the bunch of bright red gerberas he held in his hands.

'I'm Brent. And I think you must be Benji, right?'

Benji squinted at the man on the doorstep. 'How do you know that?'

'I've seen your picture in your Aunty Grace's bag.'

Grace slowed her footsteps as she drew closer to the exchange at the door. She leant against the wall on the other side of the foyer, absently drying her hands and actively eavesdropping.

'You know Aunty Grace?'

'We're old friends. We went to medical school together.'

Benji considered that for a moment. 'Are you the man who broke her heart? Mummy always said Aunty Grace never got married cos a man in medical school broke her heart.'

Brent blinked, momentarily speechless. 'Er…' What was he supposed to say to that—*Well, actually, young Benji, it was the other way round*?

If she'd been heartbroken, she certainly hadn't shown it. Echoes of her unemotional severing of their relationship rampaged through his head. Her gutting announcement that she was leaving to complete her studies in Brisbane, far away from the distraction of him, clanging like a great gong in his brain.

Grace straightened and dashed from her hiding place to rescue Brent. 'Benji,' she said, sidling up quickly, slipping her hands onto his little shoulders and avoiding looking at Brent altogether, 'here you are. I think Uncle Marshall's looking for you.'

Benji smiled at his aunt. 'I told him I was the best at lighting fires. He said he might need my help.'

'Okay. But be careful,' she called after him, a familiar clutch of worry grabbing at her gut. What was it about boys and fire? Marshall was as fascinated by it now, at thirty-five, as he had been at Benji's age!

She turned back to Brent, who was still standing in the doorway. Filling the doorway actually, the warm day outside blocked from her view. He was wearing jeans and a casual navy T-shirt that hung out over his waistband. It moulded his biceps and stretched nicely across his shoulders, pecs and abs.

He looked all warm and relaxed and utterly sexy with his cleanly shaven jaw and some amazing scent that made her want to track down its origin.

With her tongue.

'Sorry about the Spanish Inquisition. I'm learning that seven-year-olds don't have much of a filter.'

Brent held her gaze. 'Is it true?'

She contemplated playing dumb but she'd never been very good at artifice. She shrugged. 'I never got married because I was busy building a career. You know I never wanted the whole white-picket-fence thing and I've never regretted my choices. Julie is a romantic who thinks everyone should be married.'

Brent held his breath at her slip and watched as it dawned on her face. Watched the flash of grief streak through her eyes like a lightning bolt. He noticed the red rimming her eyes. Had she been crying? Family events like this had to be difficult.

'Was,' Grace corrected herself.

Brent didn't say anything for a moment. 'You've been crying.'

Grace frowned, his words dragging her back from an emotional abyss. 'No,' she shook her head. 'Onions. I've been chopping onions.'

'Oh,' he said, and laughed. 'Sorry.'

She smiled back at him. 'No, I'm sorry. I'm being a very bad hostess.' She held her arms out for the flowers. 'Thanks for these, they're lovely.'

'Oh,' Brent said again, looking from her to the flowers and back again. 'Sorry, I actually brought them for your mother.'

It was Grace's turn to laugh this time. 'Whoops. That was embarrassing. Sorry.' And then she laughed again.

Brent grinned, relieved to see the shadows gone from her eyes. 'So are we going to stand in the doorway and trade apologies all day or can I come in?'

Grace slapped her hand to her forehead. 'Of course, come in.'

She stepped aside and admitted him, a magical mix of aromas wafting past her—flowers, sunshine and something quintessentially male. She drew it deep into her lungs and felt a corresponding tingle in her blood. Her mouth started to salivate as if she'd just walked past a bakery and spied a very tempting pastry.

'This way,' she said, keeping a safe distance between them as she led him through the house.

It felt strange having him here again. It gave her a weird sense of déjà vu—almost like the first time she'd brought him home. Her new boyfriend. Her first proper boyfriend.

She'd been nervous then too. But for different reasons. She'd wanted him to like the sprawling home she'd grown up in. Her father, a carpenter by trade, had added to it over the years in several different renovations to create more room for his ever-growing family. It wasn't very conventional.

And she'd desperately wanted him to like her family.

She'd been acutely aware that his childhood had been very different from hers. And she'd been scared that he would run a mile after witnessing the chaos of it all. Her youngest sibling, Barry, had only been four years old. Five of her siblings had still been in primary school. It had been a lot to ask anyone to digest.

But Brent had embraced it all—family, crazy mishmash

house and all the associated noise. She'd fallen in love with him that day.

Brent followed her through a house he hadn't set foot in for over two decades. One that was still surprisingly familiar. Happy memories of family dinners and many noisy nights of babysitting. Finally getting the last child to bed and then making out on the couch in front of the television.

He smiled to himself as his gaze drifted to the swing of Grace's backside. Her hips had always been generously curved but were even more so now, with maturity on her side. Her jeans skimmed and hugged in all the right places.

It made him want to get her out of them.

Really, really badly.

Except, of course, they were friends.

She stopped just inside the back door and turned abruptly. He started guiltily, dragging his gaze up to her face. But it snagged momentarily on the way her red V-necked T-shirt stretched across her breasts. Those babies had always balanced out her hips perfectly.

Grace sucked in a breath as his eyes moved upwards, lingering on her cleavage. It was such a physical force it was as if his breath had fanned over her instead of his gaze. She willed her nipples not to react but it was futile.

Then his gaze met hers and there was a moment when everything else fell away and mutual sexual attraction roared into the silence between them.

Grace swallowed. *Pull yourself together!*

She cleared her throat and placed her hand on the doorknob. The noise outside was muffled but more than evident and she was grateful for it to help focus her scattered thoughts.

'I suppose you've forgotten how crazy it was around here all those years ago?'

Brent concentrated on the racket beyond the door and not his pounding chest or the uncomfortable tightness of his jeans. He smiled. 'No, I haven't. I loved the craziness.'

She nodded. He had. He really had. 'Good, cos it's multiplied considerably.'

He shrugged. 'Bring it on.'

Grace rolled her eyes. 'Don't say I didn't warn you.'

And then she turned and opened the door and stepped into the tornado that was a Perry family get-together.

There was a moment when the entire activity in the back yard ceased and all eyes flew to the open doorway. Like some bizarre sixth sense, the family had all smelled new blood.

Then cries of 'Brent!' rang out and he was sucked into the vortex.

'For you,' he said to Grace's mother, presenting the flowers.

'Oh, Brent, they're lovely,' Trish said, plonking a kiss on his cheek.

'You always were a crawler,' Marshall said, slapping Brent on the back and shaking his hand.

'Wendy, you're closest—could you pop these in some water, please?'

'Here, I will,' Grace volunteered, relieving her sister of the job gratefully as Brent was drawn into a bear hug by her father.

Grace faded back into the house to fill a vase at the sink. The large picture window in front of her gave her a full Technicolor view of the backyard, which made it impossible to ignore the activity.

Brent was being greeted like a long-lost son. Even Barry, who'd been six years old when she'd left for Brisbane and surely wouldn't remember Brent at all, was shaking Brent's hand with vigour.

Grace's heart gave a painful squeeze. Were they all just filling the gap today?

The Julie gap?

It was plain wrong to have everyone here except her.

They'd spent the last hour pretending there wasn't a great big gaping hole in their family unit. Because that's what they did now. Laughing and joking. Talking and telling jokes and being positive.

And being loud. As loud as possible.

Pretending.

For each other. For Tash and Benji.

Trying to be *normal.*

And Grace was sure, from the outside at least, they would have appeared quite normal. Just a regular, albeit rather large, suburban family having a regular weekend celebration in the back yard.

But the hole never really went away.

Maybe having Brent back helped. Maybe it took them all back to happier times? When the family had been complete and nothing could touch them.

The good old days.

As for Brent, he was lapping it up. Grace smiled despite the heaviness in her heart and her misgivings about him being there.

Misgivings totally justified after their moment at the door.

It was as if he'd never left, slipping into his *Grace's boyfriend* shoes and making himself comfy.

Except he wasn't.

And he wasn't Julie either.

Grace pulled herself out of her funk and rejoined the Perry clan. 'Here she is,' Trish proclaimed. 'We were about to send out a search party.'

'I see you've met everyone, then,' Grace said.

He smiled at her as he passed her a boutique beer. She took it, the frosty glass a stark contrast to the warmth pulsing through her everywhere at the sheer sexiness of his smiling face.

'There are a few more of you than the last time I was here.' He grinned.

'We're going to test you in an hour,' Trish teased.

Brent let out a hoot of laughter. 'Oh, I see. I have to earn my supper.'

'Around here you do.' Grace's father grinned.

'I see the old tree house is still going strong, Lucas,' Brent said to Grace's father.

He took in the sight of the enormous sycamore tree that dominated one corner of the large back yard, branching over the fences on either side and providing shade for several sets of neighbours also. It was truly magnificent.

The tree house was just as grand. The Swiss Family Robinson couldn't have built a better one. Brent raised the beer bottle to his mouth to hide the smile that came to his lips as he remembered the night he and Grace had made love in the tree house.

'Yep. Grandkids use it now.'

Tash approached, her permanent scowl firmly in place, and Grace tensed. 'Everything okay, Tash? We should be eating soon.'

Before she could acknowledge—or ignore—Grace, Brent jumped in. 'Ah, so this is Tash,' he said, holding out his hand. He would never have recognised this girl as the smiling girl with long blonde hair from the photo. 'Nice to meet you.'

Tash blinked and Grace watched as her niece's lips parted slightly and the scowl slipped. A sort of stunned look took its place and she even managed a small smile.

Grace couldn't believe the transformation. Although she could understand the impetus. Brent Cartwright seemed to have that effect on all women. From toddlers to grannies.

Tash darted a nervous look in Grace's direction. 'You'... seen a photo of me?'

Grace knew exactly what she was thinking—*Oh my God, what was I wearing? How old was I? It wasn't that naked-in-the-backyard-pool one, was it?*

'Your Aunty Grace showed me. I thought how much you looked like her but now I've seen you in the flesh you're the spitting image of Julie.'

Grace heard her mother's indrawn breath as her own muscles tightened to an unbearable tension.

'You...knew Mum?'

Brent flicked a glance towards Grace and Trish, who had visibly paled. 'I did. She was fantastic.' He paused, unsure of what to say. 'The world is a poorer place without her.'

Tash stared for a moment or two then Trish jumped in. 'Okay, then, come on, love.' She ruffled Tash's hair. 'Let's go and see how those snags are doing.'

Tash let herself be bundled along and Brent watched them go. 'I'm sorry.' He grimaced, looking down at Grace. 'Did I say the wrong thing?'

Grace shook her head. 'Not at all. We're all walking on eggshells around her. She usually hates to even hear Julie's name mentioned. We never quite know how she'll react.'

'Has she had counselling?'

Grace nodded. 'A couple of times. But then she refused to go.'

Brent heard the sadness weighing down Grace's voice. It was unbearable. 'She needs to be able to talk about her mum.'

Grace felt a prickle of resentment. 'I know that.' She was a doctor, for crying out loud. Didn't he think she knew that? 'I'm just trying to take one day at a time,' she said defensively.

What clue would he have? A footloose, fancy-free bachelor? She was doing the best she could, damn it. She'd been living a single woman's life all her adult years and had never been blessed with maternal instincts. This was all new to her.

Brent nodded. 'I'm sorry, I didn't mean to criticise. You'll get through this. I know you will.'

And because she looked like she needed it, he put his arm around her shoulder and pulled her into him. He was surprised when she plonked her head against his shoulder, accepting his comfort with no resistance.

It was just like the old days.

She must be worn down.

Grace shut her eyes, briefly letting his warmth and his solidness and his deep reassurance ease the worry lashing her insides.

'Who's for cricket?' Marshall yelled above the din, hitting a tennis ball high into the air with a bat.

A deafening affirmative response followed and Brent gave her arm a squeeze. 'Gotta go whip some Perry butt.'

Grace laughed. 'Good luck with that.'

They grinned at each other for a moment and Grace's heart rate spiked. Then he was away and she absently rubbed at her suddenly cold arms.

It was seven o'clock before Grace knew it and the crowd was starting to thin. Tired Perry children were being bundled up by their parents in preparation for home and everyone was in clean-up mode. The night air made her shiver despite the warmth of the afternoon and she had to remind herself she wasn't living in the Sunshine State any more.

'You don't have to clean up, Brent,' she said, as he pulled up beside her and started to gather plates.

'Nonsense,' he said. 'I helped make the mess. I can help clean it up.'

Grace laughed. 'Oh I'm sure we noticed your mess amongst the thirty-odd kids' plates and debris scattered everywhere.'

'Aunty Grace?'

Grace turned to find Tash standing behind her. She was fidgeting with her mobile phone in her hands and not quite making eye contact. Grace quelled the impulse to tense and smiled at her niece. 'Yes?'

'I'm off to the movies. I'll be back by eleven.'

Grace blinked. Her pulse beat loudly in her ears as Tash threw the fait accompli at her like a great big rock.

Grace took a breath. *She's a teenager. She's testing the boundaries. It's normal.*

Grace folded her arms. 'Er…no. No, you're not.'

Tash stood her ground. 'Yes, I am.'

The tips of Grace's fingers dug into the flesh of her arms. 'It's Sunday night. Tomorrow is a school day.'

Tash glared at her aunt. 'I'm not a little kid.'

'No, you're not. But you still have to follow the rules.'

'The rules suck,' Tash said belligerently.

Grace nodded. 'Yep. Mostly they do.'

'Please, Aunty Grace. Just this once,' she wheedled.

Grace blinked at her niece's rapid-fire change of tack. 'No.'

'I'll never ask again.'

Grace suppressed a snort. Would that that was true. Still, at least she was asking this time. That scary afternoon she'd run off and Grace hadn't been able to find her for hours had aged her a decade. 'And how do you propose to get there? And who exactly are you going with, Tash?'

Tash was back to belligerent as she gave a careless shrug. 'Some kids from school.'

'Do they have names?'

Tash's lips tightened. 'Just kids. Friends.'

Grace drew in a breath, reaching for patience. 'Trinny and Simone and Justine?'

Tash shook her head. 'New friends.'

Grace felt her unease grow. Since she'd been back Tash had shunned her old friends. It was concerning—old friends were part of the reason for moving the kids back to Melbourne.

'If you want to go to the movies next weekend, I'm sure we could arrange it. But I'll need to meet your friends first and know transport details. I'd also like phone numbers for their parents.'

An incredulous look came over Tash's face as if Grace had asked her to provide police background checks and urine samples for drug screening. 'That's bloody ridiculous,' Tash yelled. Tears welled in her eyes. 'Mum would have let me go.'

Grace sucked in a breath as Tash's accusation slammed into her. She felt a warm hand on her shoulder. It glided up the slope of her neck coming to rest at her nape. She turned to see Brent gazing at her, sympathy in his eyes. She'd almost forgotten he was there.

Almost forgotten everyone was there, busying themselves

with the cleaning and trying not to listen to the conversation between Tash and Grace. But the sudden shocked silence spoke volumes.

Grace looked at Tash, her heart breaking as tears trekked down her niece's face. 'I think we both know, that's not true, Natasha.'

'How do you know?' Tash yelled. 'You were never around anyway.'

'Natasha!' a shocked Trish gasped.

Tash glanced guiltily at her grandmother before looking back at Grace. 'Oh, forget it,' Tash snarled, dashing the tears away with angry strokes. 'Just forget it.' And she stormed past them both heading to the tree house.

Brent placed a restraining hand on her arm as Grace turned to follow her. 'Leave her to cool down,' he urged.

Grace was shaking on the inside from the confrontation, from the venom in her niece's accusation. 'But she's crying. I can't bear it when she cries.'

The anguish in her eyes was evident. 'I know,' he said, his thumb circling against the skin of her upper arm. 'Just give her a bit of space. Half an hour. Then talk to her.'

'He's right, darling,' Trish said.

Grace knew they were right but it didn't stop her wanting to go to Tash anyway. 'Okay.' She sighed. 'I'll help clean up then I'll go to her.'

CHAPTER SIX

THREE quarters of an hour later, Grace drained the dirty water from the sink, her gaze flicking beyond the window to the darkened tree house for the hundredth time.

Dread at the conversation she needed to have was churning in her stomach like bricks in a tumbledryer.

How was she supposed to handle this?

'That's the last one,' Brent said, as he dried the sole remaining plate.

They were the only ones in the kitchen, standing side by side at the sink. The others had all left in a noisy flurry and he'd shooed Grace's parents out, picking up a tea towel and ordering them to relax. Benji had been out on his feet and had gone to bed half an hour ago.

So he'd been left to prattle on with what turned out to be a very one-sided conversation.

He placed the dried plate on the bench and moved to stand behind Grace, his hands sliding to the taut muscles either side of her neck. He looked out at the tree house, rubbing absently at the knots in her traps, his chin on her head.

'Why don't you let me go and speak to her?'

Grace stirred from her reverie. As nice as it was to lean into him, to have his heat at her back, she couldn't shirk this responsibility—no matter how much she wanted to. 'No. I'll do it.'

She sounded like she was about to walk in front of a firing squad. 'I'm serious. Sometimes it's easier to talk to someone who isn't so close.'

Grace was tempted. So tempted. To abdicate this to someone else…

Could she?

'At least let me try. I might be able to break the ice.'

Grace felt a wave of gratitude swamp her as she let go of the must-do-it-myself ideal. Maybe Brent was right.

'Okay,' she murmured, pulling away from him.

A few minutes later they stepped out into the brisk night air. Grace was pleased she'd donned a cardigan. She headed for the old wooden swing that hung beneath the tree house as Brent climbed up the ladder. The swing creaked a little as she sat on the wooden seat.

The smell of aged hessian filled her nostrils as she leaned her cheek against the thick roughness of rope. It mingled with the lingering aromas of cooked meat and wood smoke and transported her back to her childhood. If she shut her eyes, she could be fifteen again.

Tash's age.

Her heart gave a painful squeeze as a jumble of emotions took hold. Helplessness, anger, frustration.

Overwhelming sadness.

Poor Tash.

She heard the tread of Brent's foot on the wooden ladder that was as solid today as it had been the day her father had built it when they'd first moved to the house. Grace had been six years old.

Then she heard a knock from above and Brent asking if he could enter. His voice carried easily through the tree house's open windows and out into the stillness of the night.

Tash murmured something unintelligible and Grace heard Brent's steps and a shuffling as he settled somewhere.

She crossed her fingers.

Brent, his eyes adjusting to the dark, sat on the floor opposite Tash in the large hexagonal structure. It was strewn with pieces of plastic furniture—tables, chairs, a large plastic kitchen ensemble, free-standing shelves and cupboards pushed against walls—and kids' toys.

He placed his palms on the floor as he lowered himself down and felt something gritty scratching him. Sand from the sandpit below, no doubt. He wiped his palms absently on his jeans.

Tash, her legs drawn up to her chin, had a big crocheted blanket thrown over her knees, one of many, by the looks of it, stashed in a beat up old cupboard beside her.

'I suppose you're here to *express your disappointment*,' Tash said after a moment or two, raising her hands in the air and mimicking quote marks.

'Nope.'

'Going to give me some lame you'll-get-over-it speech?'

'Nope.'

'Not even "I'm sorry for your loss"? Or "Things will get easier"?' Tash gave a harsh laugh. 'God, I hate hearing those trite, unoriginal words. Don't people realise how underwhelming they are? Like I lost a bloody library book or my mobile phone.'

'Nope.' Brent shook his head. 'Not going to say that either. I think this whole thing sucks. Big time. That you and Benji got a raw deal. I wish I could make that better for you. Everyone does. I know Grace does. But unfortunately you've got to do all the hard yards yourself.'

Tash squinted at him. 'You're not a psychiatrist, are you?'

Brent laughed. 'No.'

'Good. Cos you really suck at it.'

Brent chuckled again and they lapsed into a short silence.

'It just doesn't feel right without them,' Tash said. 'Being here, all together.'

Brent nodded. 'I imagine it's going to feel like that for a long time. Maybe it always will.'

Tash drew the blanket up to her chin, observing him for a while. 'Do your parents live in Melbourne?'

Brent shrugged. 'I don't know. I've never known my parents.

I was abandoned as a child and spent all my life in foster homes.'

Tash sat up, the blanket falling down to her knees. She stared at him. 'Really? Oh, God, I'm so sorry...'

Brent raised an eyebrow. 'For my loss?' He smiled.

Tash started to say something else and then stopped, realising that Brent was teasing. 'Yeah, yeah.' She smiled and pulled the blanket back over her shoulders again.

They sat in more silence, which was eventually broken by Tash. 'Tell me a memory.'

Brent frowned. Did she want one from his childhood? Such as it was? He could, of course, tell her his one abiding memory of this tree house but it was hardly appropriate. 'Care to narrow that down?'

'You knew my mum, right? Tell me a memory.'

Ah.

Brent sifted through myriad images in his mind, twisting them and turning them over like an emotional kaleidoscope, trying to find one that best captured Julie's essence.

'I remember us all heading down to Bells Beach the week after she finished her final grade-twelve exams. Grace and I and Doug and Julie—'

'You knew Dad too?' Tash interrupted.

Brent nodded. 'Grace and I had been together for about six months when Doug came on the scene.' A tear spilled down Tash's cheek and he watched as she dashed it away. 'She was so happy that day. To be done with school. To be free. She kept saying, "I can't believe I'm free." She hit that beach and she cartwheeled all the way down to the ocean.'

Brent smiled at the image of Julie making Doug's day by bouncing around in that itty-bitty bikini. 'The water was absolutely freezing but she dived straight in. She didn't come out for hours.'

Tash smiled through her tears. 'She loved the ocean.'

Brent nodded again. 'Yep. She did.'

'She used to say if we won lotto we'd get a house right on

the beach.' She wiped at another tear. 'Did Dad go in the water too? He was never a huge fan.'

Brent heard the hunger in Tash's voice. Her thirst for memories was so tangible it parched his throat. He chuckled. 'A little. He was just happy to watch your mum prance around in a bikini.'

Tash screwed up her nose, trying to look put off and murmuring a quick 'Eww!' But a laugh bubbled out quickly after. 'He was always such a perv.'

She laughed again and Brent joined her. When their laughter had settled, he decided to push a little. 'You know Grace and your other aunts and uncles, your grandparents, they'd share their memories too...'

Tash sniffed. 'It hurts them. To remember. I don't want to hurt them.'

Ah.

Tash wanted to spare them pain.

Brent shrugged. 'You might be surprised.' And then, because he could feel Tash was receptive, he pushed some more. 'You know Grace is just trying to keep you safe, right? She's worried about you, Tash.'

The teenager averted her gaze, taking great interest in the crocheted holes, poking her fingers through them.

'Tash?'

'I know. I just get...so angry sometimes. It's just so...unfair, you know?' She didn't wait for his acknowledgement as she stabbed all her fingers into available holes. 'And she's always trying to talk to me about Mum and Dad, trying to get me to talk about them. She thinks it's unhealthy not to. But I don't know what to say...'

'Have you told her that?'

Tash paused. 'She won't listen to me.'

Brent doubted that very much. He also doubted that was the real reason for Tash's beef with Grace if the teenager's continuing avoidance of eye contact was any clue.

But he figured he'd probably pushed enough for one night.

And Tash obviously agreed. She stood abruptly, letting the blanket fall to the floor. 'I'm going in now.'

Brent stood also. 'Okay. It was nice talking to you.'

Tash gave him a stiff nod and headed for the door. She turned awkwardly at the last moment. 'Thanks for the memory.'

Brent inclined his head. 'Any time.' And Tash disappeared down the ladder.

Grace sat motionless on the swing, unnoticed by her niece in the dark shadows of the tree house. A tear fell unchecked down her cheek. The back door opened and a shaft of light illuminated Tash's features.

Despite her attempts to look otherwise, the yellow glow softened Tash. Her grief was there in sharp relief but the beam of light also captured a sweetness, an innocence lost.

Grace would give anything to find it again.

Brent slid back down the wall, drawing his knees up, resting his hands on his thighs. He hoped he'd said the right things. Hoped he hadn't pushed too much. In a lot of ways he related to Tash. He knew what it was like to grow up with a big part of your life missing.

He heard steps on the ladder and turned his head in time to see Grace's appearing over the lip of the doorway. Their gazes locked.

'Did you hear all that?'

Grace paused where she was on the ladder and nodded. She'd heard every word—or most of them anyway. And each one had sliced into her heart with all the surgical precision of a scalpel blade. 'I feel like such a failure,' she whispered.

She looked utterly dejected and Brent's heart swelled in his chest. Grace, the high achiever, the go-getter, was at a total loss.

'Come here.' He patted the floor beside him.

Grace hesitated only briefly before climbing the rest of the way in. She remembered all the times they'd laid together staring into the dark, talking. She talking. Him listening. Letting her vent about something at uni or some babysitting her mother wanted her to do or whatever had been bothering her at the time.

Giving her perspective.

He'd been her confidant as well as her lover.

She hadn't realised until this very moment how much she'd missed that about him. Brent had always been a great listener.

She crawled over to him on her hands and knees. It was darker inside than out but her eyes had adjusted. She sat down. Not too close. She left a respectable distance between his thigh and hers, his arm and hers.

'Yuk,' she said, rubbing her hands together. 'There's enough sand up here to open a beach.'

Brent chuckled. 'Yes, it is a little gritty, isn't it?'

Grace rolled her eyes. 'Still king of the understatement, I see.'

At one time he'd driven her nuts with his economical use of adjectives. It wasn't until she'd known him for a while she's realised that it was a trait born of his upbringing. He hadn't led a flowery life.

Listening to him talk to Tash about being abandoned as a child had released all her old feelings of impotence and sorrow. She'd been incensed on his behalf when he'd first told her about his bleak childhood. He hadn't been mistreated but he had been passed around. No chance for him to settle anywhere. No stability. No routine.

Her heart had bled for the lost little boy he'd been. But he'd just shrugged. *It is what it is.* That's what he'd said. And she'd wrapped her body around him and vowed to love him even more.

A silence settled around them as they both got lost in their own thoughts. Sounds of the night invaded the hush surrounding them. The distant noise of a car starting competed with a nearby barking dog and, somewhere in the neighbourhood, a crying child.

Brent rolled his head to the side. 'She's going to be all right, you know.' He didn't know how he knew, he just did.

He reached for her hand and entwined it with hers. It was cold and he used his other hand to encase hers completely, rubbing at it absently.

Grace looked down at their linked hands. It had been twenty years since he'd held her hand and it felt like just yesterday as the warmth from his hand travelled up her arm and reached into all the places that were cold with fear and doubt and worry.

His calm reassurance was comforting and she wanted to lay her head on his shoulder and have him tell her that over and over again.

'I hope you're right.'

Brent squeezed her hand. 'I usually am.'

Grace gave a half-laugh but felt absurdly like crying. She hadn't spoken any of her doubts out loud to anyone in eighteen months. And here she was dumping it all on an old boyfriend.

Who was now, technically, her boss.

And she didn't have a clue why.

'I can't believe the way she...' Grace's voice cracked on a jagged block of emotion that tore at her throat. She sucked in a breath to steady herself. 'The way she opened up to you.'

To her horror she felt a burning behind her eyes and a prickling in her nose. 'I mean,' she continued as the pressure built behind her eyes and in her nose and bloomed in her chest as well, 'I've been trying to get her to talk. To share things with her. Talk about Julie and Doug and...'

More emotion welled up, making it hard to talk, making her voice husky and useless. And then a tear fell, slipping under her glasses, and she dashed it away. She looked up at him.

'I have been listening. I have. I have a thousand memories I could tell her. I've tried to tell her...'

Brent ached to reach for her. Tash and Grace were both

hurting so much. 'She's trying to spare you from the pain of them, Grace,' he said gently.

Grace felt another tear well. 'She's a kid. She shouldn't have to feel responsible for my…' Grace took a breath as a great big sob threatened and her face fought the urge to crumple. 'She's not supposed to worry about me. I'm not her…responsibility.'

'Oh Gracie,' he whispered, lifting a hand from hers and catching a tear with his thumb, wiping it across her cheekbone.

And that did it. Her face did crumple. In fact, her whole body seemed to fold in on itself and before she knew it he was hauling her close, his arm around her shoulders, tucking her into his side, stroking her arm with his fingers.

Grace pressed her face into the solid warmth of his shoulder as great heaving sobs tore through her chest. They ripped open the raw jagged edges of her grief and consumed her with their ferocity.

Later she would feel embarrassed. She'd want to snatch back time and erase the entire scene. But for now she clung to his stability like he was a lighthouse and she was being tossed about in a stormy sea. And strangely it didn't seem weird. They'd been apart for twenty years and yet turning to him still seemed so natural.

Grace hadn't cried like this since the day Marshall had shown up at her work in Brisbane with the bleakest eyes she'd ever seen. The family hadn't wanted to tell her over the phone.

Not even at the funeral. Because suddenly she had two children depending on her. Looking at her with bewildered eyes for comfort and direction. For someone to tell them it was going to be okay. They'd needed her to be together.

Sure, there'd been tears, but not like this. This seemingly bottomless well of grief.

Brent held her while she wept. She'd curled into his side and was half-draped across his chest, her arm flung around his neck. He ran his fingers down her arm and her back in long, smooth strokes as his shirt absorbed her tears and his body absorbed her almost violent sobs. She rocked against him as each one squeezed the anguish from her body like a contraction and he held her tighter.

'I'm s-so s-sorry,' Grace hiccoughed between sobs.

'Shh, it's okay,' he murmured, rubbing his chin against her hair. 'Julie died. You're allowed to be sad too.'

Grace shook her head. 'I'm usually s-stronger than this.'

Brent squeezed her shoulder. 'I know how strong you are.' She'd broken up with him, hadn't she? 'You don't have to be strong around me. Just get it all out.'

Grace nodded as more emotion welled in her throat and more tears fell unchecked. She scrunched his T-shirt in her hand and took his advice.

She let it all out.

Time passed. Grace wasn't sure how long. Twenty? Thirty minutes? Her sobs eventually became sniffles and the tears slowed and then dried up. She started to become aware of other things. The warmth of a solid pec beneath her cheek, the feel of wet cotton, the steady thud of his heartbeat in her ear, the luxurious stroking of his fingers against her back.

And the intoxicating aroma of man.

She found herself inhaling deeply, sucking it into the bottom of her lungs, savouring it like an addict. She scrunched his shirt a little tighter as it made her feel slightly dizzy.

'Better now?'

His voice rumbled through his rib cage and connected with her ear. She stirred, lifting her head. She felt weary to her bones. Utterly exhausted. Wrung out. She felt like she could sleep for a week.

But, yes, she did feel better.

'Thank you. Yes.'

She straightened up. Uncurled her body from his side, supporting herself against the wall next to him. She readjusted her glasses. Their arms brushed. Their thighs were separated by the narrowest of distances.

Grace looked at him. 'I'm sorry to—'

'Don't.' It probably came out more fiercly than he'd meant

it to by the look on her face, but he couldn't bear to hear her apologise again. He looked down at her and placed his hand against her mouth. 'There's nothing to apologise for.'

She blinked up at him owl-like through her glasses and he became aware of the texture of her lip gloss beneath his fingers. He could smell it also, sugary sweet. And suddenly the memory of him kissing that gloss off her mouth in this very structure pushed into his mind.

Sneaking in here with her late one night and laying her back on a sleeping bag and loving her. Stifling her climactic cries with his mouth so they didn't wake the entire neighbourhood. Especially her parents.

Their gazes locked.

He slowly withdrew his hand.

Grace held her breath. She wondered if he was thinking what she'd been thinking. About that night…

She was aware of his arm against hers, the heat of his thigh aligned with hers, his mouth so very, very close. Grace watched as his gaze dropped to her lips. She swallowed.

They shouldn't be doing this. 'Brent…'

The huskiness in her voice, the way she said his name went straight to Brent's belly. The urge to pull her into him, to drop his mouth to hers roared in his head and he struggled to deny it.

Her mouth shimmered in the darkness. Like a great beacon. 'Is that still the same lip gloss you used to wear?'

Her breath stopped in her lungs. 'Brent.'

'Honey something it was called. I've been trying to remember since the day of the interview.'

'Honey Jumble,' she whispered.

Brent nodded. Honey Jumble. That was it. 'Does it still taste the same?'

Grace felt her pelvic floor clamp down hard. 'Brent, I—'

He didn't give her time to voice her protest as the urge to reacquaint himself with the taste of the gloss, the taste of her, overcame him. Overcame all the reasons why he shouldn't.

It had been so long and she was so close.

So Gracie.

His hand reached for her face, cupping her jaw as his lips closed the distance from hers. Honey Jumble teased his taste buds and he licked at it like it was the elixir of life.

Grace felt only a second's resistance then she was groaning against his mouth, turning slightly to wind her arms around his neck, her surrender immediate. She opened to him deeper, angled her head, pulled him closer.

It felt so very good, being in his arms again. Being kissed by him again. So familiar. It fizzed through her veins and sparked at her nerve endings. So much of her life was foreign right now but this, this was, oh, so familiar.

Brent twisted, grabbing her arms and pulling her up and over him. She went eagerly, needing no urging to open her legs, to straddle him. He ploughed one hand into her hair as the other gripped her hip, his fingers digging into a rounded buttock. His tongue pushed into her mouth as his hips pushed up against hers.

He moaned deeply as hers pushed right back.

Heat licked at him. Everywhere. His belly, his thighs, his groin. Flame rolled through his veins and arteries and burned behind his eyes. He was so damn hot.

So damn hard.

He pushed his hand up from her hip under her T-shirt, feeling the dip of her back and the smooth warmness of her skin in contrast to the ridges of her spine. He wanted to touch her everywhere. Feel her touching him.

'Grace? Grace?' A distant voice from the direction of the house broke into their intimacy. 'Benji's woken up. He's crying. He's asking for you.'

Brent pulled abruptly away as if Trish had thrown a bucket of cold water over him. Grace whimpered softly in protest and he almost groaned out loud.

'Shh,' he murmured, their foreheads touching, his thumb

stroking her moist lips smeared with honey and him. His breathing was rough and loud in the confined space. As was hers.

Her chest heaved against his as they both struggled for air. Squashed against him, the evidence of his arousal was distracting as hell. It was tempting. So tempting to ignore her mother's call and just reach down and unzip him.

A few seconds was all it would take to reacquaint herself with all his glorious length.

But it wasn't just about her any more.

She lifted her head from Brent's. 'I'll be right there,' she yelled in the direction of the nearest window.

Grace heard the kitchen window shut and she looked back at Brent. His mouth was moist and his hair was well and truly ruffled.

'You should go.'

Grace nodded. 'You're angry, aren't you?'

'Nope.' Not at her anyway. At himself. He didn't want this. She'd walked out on him years ago and he was over her.

Grace shifted off him. 'This is my life now, Brent. I don't have room for any of this.'

'I know,' he said.

Then he hauled his butt off the floor, holding out a hand to help her up.

CHAPTER SEVEN

HALF an hour later Grace eased herself off Benji's bed. She'd cuddled him and read him a book and stayed with him until he'd fallen asleep. He was breathing evenly now and she stroked his forehead, pushing his fringe back off his face.

He had bad dreams about a car on fire and Julie's voice calling his name from somewhere amongst the flames.

The counsellor said it could take a while for them to become less frequent and that it was possible he could have them for ever.

Grace shuddered at the thought. Poor Benji. He was so little. Too little for all this.

She left his lamp on and switched out the overhead light as she wandered towards the lounge room. Her thoughts returned to Brent and what had transpired earlier in the back yard.

A momentary aberration.

A mistake.

She was surprised to hear the low rumble of Brent's voice as she approached the lounge room. He was supposed to be gone. She stood in the doorway unannounced for a moment. Brent and her father were sitting in the recliners, their backs to the door. Her mother and Tash were sharing the three-seater.

They were all chatting away like Brent had never left their lives. Like the intervening twenty years had never happened. Her mother said something. Brent laughed. Tash joined in.

It was way too cosy for her liking.

'Oh, there you are, darling,' Trish said, suddenly noticing Grace leaning against the doorjamb.

Brent looked over his shoulder. Grace was frowning and

he didn't need his medical degree to figure out why. He rose quickly.

'Right, well, I'd best be off, then,' he said.

The family stood, all talking at once, urging him not to be a stranger.

'He can come to our house-warming, right, Aunty Grace?'

Grace blinked. 'We're having a house-warming?'

'Of course,' Tash said. 'I can invite my friends over—that way you'll get to know them.'

Grace slid a sideways glance at Brent. Was this progress? She looked back at Tash and saw the plea in her eyes.

'Well, I suppose so...but you'll want to do the renovations to your bedroom first, right? Don't want anyone seeing that hideous wallpaper.'

Tash agreed quickly. 'Oh, God, no. But that should only take a weekend once we're in. Hey...' she turned to Brent '...maybe you could help—'

'Tash!' Grace admonished quickly. 'Brent is a very busy person. With his own life.'

Brent chuckled for Tash's benefit but got the not-so-hidden message. 'It's all right. I'm pretty sure I can help out with a bit of DIY.'

Tash grinned and Grace rolled her eyes. 'Well, we'll see,' she said. 'Say goodbye, Tash.'

Brent made his farewells and followed Grace to the door, stepping out as she opened it, his brain fixated on their kiss. What had happened in the tree house had been an anomaly, he reminded himself. The result of an overwrought Grace colliding with a hefty dose of nostalgia. That was all.

He turned to face her.

'Thanks for taking the time with Tash today. I really *do* appreciate it. I understand that the dramas of a fifteen-year-old girl probably aren't in your field of expertise.'

Brent shrugged. 'It was no bother.'

Her breath caught in her throat at the husky note in his voice, which did crazy things to her pulse. She could almost feel his hand beneath her T-shirt again, his erection pressing into her.

God, what must he think of her instantaneous surrender? That she'd been pining for his touch for two decades? She took a step towards him, flicking a quick glance over her shoulder for any nearby flapping ears. Maybe she could explain?

And then she could explain it to herself!

'About before. In the tree house—'

Brent held up a hand. 'Don't worry about it. I understand. It was... There are a lot of memories up there. It was a slip, that's all.'

Grace nodded. A slip. Yes, that's what it was. 'Absolutely.'

'So, let's just forget it, okay?'

'Oh, yes, please.' Grace nodded again, relief flooding through her veins at his casual dismissal of what had transpired between them.

Brent chuckled at her palpable relief. 'Good. See you in a few days.'

He didn't wait for an acknowledgement and she watched as he turned away and trudged down the path.

Three days later Grace was behind a cubicle curtain, demonstrating to Adam Mather how to reduce a dislocated shoulder, when Brent tracked her down. Her eyes met his when he stepped in and she caught a glimpse of something raw and unguarded in his hazel gaze as the memory of their kiss slithered into the space between them before they slipped into their professional guises.

'Can I help you, Dr Cartwright?'

Brent shook his head. 'Ellen said you needed me?'

Grace blushed at his choice of words after their passionate clinch on Sunday night. She looked away quickly. She had asked the NUM when he'd be in but she hadn't meant for it to be a thing.

She'd thought she ought to take the temperature of their relationship after Sunday night but now Abby, the nurse who was assisting them, was looking at her curiously and she was annoyed at herself for saying anything at all.

'Oh, yes. I just needed a quick word.' For Abby's sake she added, 'It wasn't anything important.'

Brent nodded briskly, ignoring the stirrings caused by her Honey Jumble lips. 'What have you got?'

'Dr Mather?' Grace prompted.

'Forty-five-year-old male cyclist came off his bike, falling heavily on his left shoulder.' Adam slipped into presenting mode with ease. 'The position indicates a complete dislocation and the X-ray confirms it.'

Brent crossed to the illuminated viewing box onto which the X-rays were clipped. He studied them, noting immediately the obvious dislocation of the humeral head but paying closer attention for the presence of any fractures that would complicate the reduction process.

'The X-ray, as you can see, is clear of fractures,' Adam continued, 'and this is the patient's first presentation with this type of injury.'

Brent crossed back to the patient and smiled at the very fit, middle-aged man half out of his Lycra cyclist's gear. His face was tense and looking at the gross deformity of his shoulder Brent didn't blame him.

'Hi…' Brent looked at the patient's chart. 'Graham. Pain bad?'

Graham nodded. 'Terrible. Worse than my wife's three labours. But don't tell her that.'

Brent chuckled. 'I'll keep it between us. Sit tight. It'll all be over in a couple of minutes.'

Brent looked back at Adam and he continued. 'The ambulance gave him Penthrane. We've inserted a cannula and are about to administer midazolam for the procedure.'

'All right, then, I'll leave you to it.'

The curtain flicked back and Ellen appeared. 'Abby? You were supposed to go on your lunch break ten minutes ago.'

'Sorry,' she said, indicating the tray of drugs she'd drawn up ready to administer. 'I got a little held up.'

Brent looked sheepishly at the harassed-looking NUM. 'Sorry, that's my fault. You go to lunch, Abs. I'll give the drugs.'

Abs? Grace kept her face impassive at the easy familiarity. Did he make a habit of giving all the women he knew pet names?

Abs. Gabs.

Gracie.

'Thank you, Brent,' Ellen said. 'The least you can do,' she said with mock severity, before snapping the curtain back in place.

Brent chuckled as he took the green plastic tray from Abby and read the colour-coded labels attached to the drugs.

'Okay.' He nodded. 'I'm ready when you are.'

Grace indicated to Adam to take up position beside Graham. She nodded at Brent to administer the drugs.

'Okay, Graham, you'll feel sleepy and a little bit drifty for a while and that's when we'll pop this sucker back in. Let us know if you feel any pain during the procedure and we can top you up, all right?'

Graham nodded. 'Just do it,' he said, his words slurring. 'Just get it ov...'

Within seconds Graham had drifted into a light sleep, his eyes fluttering shut. 'Okay, Adam, you're on.'

Brent watched as Grace stood behind the resident, talking him through the procedure. He was impressed. A lot of doctors would have taught through example, through demonstrating the actions themselves, but Brent knew the best way to learn, the only way really, was by hands-on experience.

She showed Adam where to place his hands and how to apply traction while abducting and performing external rotation at the same time. She also warned him that, despite his sedated state, Graham might cry out when the humeral head slipped back into place.

Brent had known since the first day, when she'd cracked open that chest, he'd made the right decision in employing her, but this was the first time he'd seen her in a teaching role and his conviction was only strengthened. The Central was a major teaching hospital and she was a tremendous teacher.

Adam was nervous—having not one but two consultants watch you perform a procedure for the first time would give even the most confident resident the jitters—but she set him at ease. She didn't rush him or try to take over when he fumbled, and she congratulated him when he got each step right.

And when the joint finally clicked back into place and Graham cried out briefly in pain, giving Adam a scare, she clapped and grinned at him. As Brent gave some pain relief Grace said 'You did it. Congratulations, Dr Mather, you just reduced your first shoulder.'

Adam's answering smile said it all. 'Thanks, Grace. That was… Wow…' He ran his hands through his hair. 'That was amazing.'

Grace poked his chest playfully. 'You were amazing.'

Brent watched as they grinned at each other, feeling curiously left out. Then Graham stirred and Grace got back to business.

'We'll need a check X-ray,' she said to Adam, 'and then we'll pop it in a sling for discharge.'

Brent slipped away as the teaching continued.

Twenty minutes later Grace found Brent in his office, talking on the phone. He looked up as she stood in his doorway and he gestured her in. Grace took a seat, waiting while he finished his call. He looked very autumnal in his rusty gold shirt and a tawny tie the colour of an eagle's eye.

With his stethoscope slung around his neck, drawing attention to broad shoulders, he looked like a television doctor—sexy and god-like.

Brent ended the call and smiled at her. 'Great job with Adam,' he said. 'You're a good teacher.'

Grace felt her cheeks warm at his compliment and she smiled. 'Thanks. I enjoy it.'

He inclined his head. 'I can tell. Have you ever thought about lecturing?'

She nodded. 'I've toyed with it. Particularly when the kids came to live with me—better hours, all school holidays off. But I'd miss the vibe of the hands-on stuff.'

Brent completely understood. 'Yep. Totally.' He'd be bored in a minute with no patients to treat, no lives to save.

They sat for a moment in mutual agreement. 'So...you wanted to see me?' he prompted.

Clunk. The glow from Adam's successful performance disappeared and it was back to real life. She sat up and smoothed her trousers over her knee.

'Yes.' She looked over her shoulder at the open door. Why hadn't she shut it?

Because she hadn't wanted anyone to think anything untoward...

'I...I just wanted to check we're okay after the ki...after the other night.'

Brent felt the tempo of his heart rate pick up. Okay? Not really. He'd replayed that scene over and over in his head a million times. Dreamt about it.

'Cos I've been thinking,' Grace proceeded into the silence. 'It's like you said, it was a...slip. It was probably bound to happen really...given our history. Maybe we needed it to happen. To, you know, get it out of our systems.'

Brent was pretty damn sure from four nights of erotic dreams, all disconcertingly taking place in a tree house full of kids' toys, that nothing but full head-banging sex was going to *get it out of his system.*

'But I want to assure you that it won't happen again. I was a bit of a...mess, really. Well, I don't need to tell you that, do I? You just caught me at a really low point and it was easy to slip back into...old habits.'

Brent nodded. It hadn't taken his psychology major to figure out the kiss had been something familiar for her to reach for. Like an old teddy bear. He was just grateful she hadn't said bad habits.

'I'm aware though that my actions...my kissing you so... passionately...could be misconstrued. So I really need you to know that I'm not in the market for a relationship. I just don't have the time or space, emotional space, in my life for another human being. As you saw on Sunday night, I have my hands very full with two grieving kids and they need my undivided attention.'

Grace had no idea how garbled this was all coming out, she just knew she had to get it out. Put it all on the table. So she ploughed on.

'With everything so chaotic in my personal life and you know how much I hate chaos, it's important to me that one aspect of my life is stable. And for me that's work. Coming here gives me much-needed respite from home. I get to feel in control for eight hours. And I need that. So I don't need any... weirdness here at work. I don't want anything to affect our work relationship. I know we'd talked about being friends but first and foremost this relationship...' she pointed back and forth between them several times '...our professional relationship is paramount.'

Grace looked at a continuing silent Brent. 'Oh, God, please say something.'

Brent exhaled loudly. 'You haven't really given me a chance.'

Grace castigated herself for prattling. 'Sorry.'

Brent collected his thoughts for a moment. 'I agree that our professional relationship is important and also don't want anything to jeopardise it either so please don't worry.'

Grace sagged against the chair, the relief overwhelming. It flooded through her entire body like a heroin high. 'Good.'

'As for me reading anything into our kiss...' He saw Grace tense and felt a corresponding tension in his neck and shoulders. 'I understand that Sunday night was a physical manifestation of an emotional day. I hadn't read any more into it than that.'

The high spun through Grace's head until she felt almost dizzy. She smiled at him. 'Good. I'm glad. I've been worried about it.'

Dazzled by her full-wattage smile, Brent found her obvious relief perversely irritating. It was time for him to lay some cards on the table.

'As we're being frank I'd like to say something too.'

Grace nodded. 'Sure thing.'

'It took me a couple of years to get over you, Grace. But I did. I moved on. Hell, I got married twice. And, please, don't think me rude when I tell you this, but I really need you to know that I would never make the mistake of falling for you again.'

Grace's smile slipped a little as his statement had popped the bubble she'd been floating in. *Had he considered falling for her the first time a mistake?*

'Yes, I'm still attracted to you. Yes, I'll probably want to kiss you again. But please do me a favour and resist, okay? Because you're obviously no closer to committing to someone than you were twenty years ago and I don't make the same mistake twice. Believe it or not, there are plenty of women who *do* want a relationship with me. In fact,' he lied, 'I have a date tonight.'

Grace was surprised at how much his words disconcerted her. The buzz had certainly died a quick death. In her first few days at the Central she'd heard all about his playboy reputation but to hear him confirm it elevated it above the gossip that she'd pegged it as.

'So, just to be completely transparent, I'm good with being friends and colleagues and have absolutely no interest in anything else, okay?'

Grace swallowed. It seemed so much harsher coming from him. But he was right, she wasn't in a position to commit and rekindling what they'd had didn't benefit either of them. 'Okay.'

Grace's pager beeped loudly and she started. She checked the message. 'I'd better get this.'

She stood and turned to leave. 'Oh, by the way, please don't feel that you have to help with the renovations or come to the house-warming party. Tash is really very good at emotional blackmail.' She shrugged. 'I love her to pieces, but it's true.'

Brent stood also. 'Maybe. But I think it's important to her that I come. And I'm more than happy to.'

Grace swallowed. He was such a good guy. He'd always been a good guy. They'd just wanted different things and she'd been terrified that she'd loved him so much she'd end up sacrificing her things for him and she'd be swallowed up again.

'Okay. It'll probably be a couple of weeks before anything gets started.'

He shrugged. 'Fine. Whenever. Just let me know.'

The beeper rang out again. 'Gotta go,' she said, and backed out of his office.

Brent watched her go, pleased with the outcome. They both knew where they stood. The memory of Sunday night's kiss would probably make them awkward for a bit but they'd soon get into the swing of it.

Now all he had to do was extinguish her and her Honey Jumble mouth from his dreams.

And find himself a date for tonight!

Two weeks later, Grace found herself in the middle of the shift from hell. The department was frantic and everyone, including Brent, was pitching in.

Grace was examining a thirty-two-year-old woman who had taken a tumble down her front stairs at home and fractured both the bones in one of her lower legs. Her mobile phone had slipped out of her pocket during the impact and had landed in a garden bed that lined the front path.

With her eight-month-old baby feeling abandoned and crying inconsolably in the house, the woman had dragged herself over the rocky path and in severe pain to retrieve the phone, which had landed beneath some shrubs, so she could ring for an ambulance.

It had taken her half an hour. She looked like she'd been

dragged through a hedge backwards as she apologised to Grace for the third time about her clingy little girl. Grace was trying to examine the woman's bruised ribs without much success.

'I'm so sorry,' she said, wincing as she jiggled the baby a little. 'My husband should be here soon.'

Grace smiled at the harried-looking woman, who couldn't even give in to the pain of her tib and fib fracture that was so bad it had broken the skin. Not to mention the likelihood of a rib or two. Her patient was doing what mothers did—putting her child's needs first.

'It's fine, Linda,' Grace assured her. 'This little one had a major fright too today.'

Grace ruffled the baby's hair and watched as the baby shied away, bursting into tears again as she buried her face in her mother's neck. 'I think young Penny will be sticking to you like white on rice the next few days.'

Brent was passing the cube when the baby's cries pulled him up short. There was something gut-wrenching about the noise that tugged at primal instincts and he was pulling back the curtain before his brain even registered the action.

He spied Grace immediately and allowed his body the inevitable leap it took every time he saw her. His pulse kicked up a notch and his senses became sharper as he homed in on the tiny flutter at her throat and the glisten of her lips. His mouth watered, remembering how good she tasted, and he gave himself a mental shake.

His reaction to her didn't seemed to be lessening, as he'd hoped.

Sure, their relationship had normalised considerably. They were developing a good collegial routine. Professional and courteous. And he was going to her place this weekend to help out with the kids' bedroom makeovers.

But this unchecked response of his body to hers whenever they were near was a damn nuisance. Something he didn't want and could most definitely do without. Still, no matter what he did, no matter what he told himself, it was always there. So he was going to have to learn to live with it.

He'd loved her once. There was bound to be residual… attraction.

It wasn't going to kill him.

'Well, now,' he said, his gaze shifting to the woman on the gurney and the bawling baby. 'Someone's not a happy camper.'

Grace sucked in a breath as Brent filled the small cubicle with his breadth and his deep, rumbly voice and his sheer unadulterated maleness. Her heart did a quick two-step as his charisma reached out and brushed gossamer fingers over her breasts, her thighs, her belly.

She cursed her reaction to him. How did he still have such an effect on her? She was at work with a baby screaming merry hell at her elbow, for Pete's sake. How long would it take for this unwanted surge of lust to die a natural death?

She watched as Brent cooed at the little girl, flashed his penlight at her and, as she reached for the light, plucked the unprotesting bundle into his arms.

Grace's heart went thunk, thunk, boom.

'She likes you.' Linda smiled.

'Of course she does.' Brent grinned at the baby and handed over the torch, which she promptly stuck in her mouth. 'What's not to like?'

He turned to face her and Grace nodded her head absently. *What indeed?*

Certainly not seeing him with a baby. She caught her breath as Penny smiled up at him around his pen. She made a grab for his ID, which hung from a lanyard around his neck, and transferred her dribbly attention to it.

And suddenly sexy went to a whole new level.

Watching him with the babe was like a sucker punch to Grace's solar plexus and she had difficulty breathing. He looked amazing with a baby—he was so big and broad compared to the wee little sprite in his arms and it magnified his masculinity tenfold.

Grace remembered how desperately he'd wanted his own family. Children to love and spoil. To give a life he'd always craved and never known.

Looking at him now, she had no doubt he would have been an excellent father. In fact, she'd never had any doubt. Visions of him piggy-backing a squealing, giggly four-year-old Barry around their house during babysitting episodes came back to her. He'd always been excellent with kids.

A funny niggling feeling teased at the periphery of her consciousness as she glimpsed a life she could have known. He looked so confident with Penny, so at ease, she could imagine him with their daughter smiling up at him like he was the centre of her universe.

Grace's breath caught in her throat as the sheer beauty of the vision pierced her to the core. An emotion she couldn't identify—didn't want to identify—welled in her chest.

But it felt eerily like melancholy.

He'd already told her that he'd never found the right person. That it *just hadn't happened*. But looking at his big hand spread securely across the baby's back it made her wonder. Late at night, when he was lying alone in his bed, did he have regrets?

Like she was having now?

But thoughts of him in bed, alone or not alone for that matter, were not good for her equilibrium and Grace was pleased when Linda said, 'Now's your chance, Dr Perry, I'm not sure how long peace will reign.'

CHAPTER EIGHT

EVENING had darkened the sky to a velvety blush several hours later when Brent popped his head into the minor ops rooms to find Grace stapling a head laceration from a workplace accident. Ellen was assisting.

'Ah, good, Ellen, you're a hard woman to track down.'

Grace looked up, her steady hand suddenly slightly shaky, and she thanked her lucky stars she was holding a stapler, not a curved blade with a suture attached. She looked beyond his shoulder and saw Donna, an agency nurse who'd been doing a lot of work in the department lately, hovering closely behind, obviously not dressed for work.

Dressed for fun.

A swift, hot dart of emotion jabbed at her diaphragm and her breath hitched.

Ellen looked up too, also not missing Donna. 'You've got me,' she said, flicking her gaze back to the job at hand, using forceps to bring the jagged edges of the head wound together for Grace to staple in place.

'Just letting you know I'm off for the night.' Brent frowned. 'Grace, shouldn't you be done by now? I'd thought you'd already gone?'

She didn't bother to raise her head again. Didn't want to see him all cosy with a woman dressed for fun. 'Just doing this last job.'

Brent felt Donna's hand on his shoulder and for some reason he tensed. 'Good.' He checked his watch, the action displacing his date's hand. 'What time on Saturday?' he asked.

Grace gripped the instrument in her hand a little tighter.

'Whenever you can get there,' she said casually. 'If something comes up, no sweat.'

'I'll be there,' he said.

The finality in his voice was unmistakeable and this time she did look up. 'Okay, see you then.'

He nodded and Grace just caught a glimpse of Donna slipping her hand into Brent's as he turned and walked away.

Her diaphragm twinged again.

Grace looked at the empty hallway for a moment before returning her attention to the patient, whose head was obscured by several green drapes. 'How are you doing under there, Jock?' she asked.

'I'm fine, lassie.'

Grace smiled at the broad accent. Jock had called Australia home for thirty years but hadn't managed to lose any of his thick Scottish brogue.

'Okay. I'm about halfway,' she said, inspecting the laceration that went from occipit to temple. 'We'll have you done in a jiffy.'

Jock grunted. The wound had been inflicted by falling debris at a work site and the Scotsman had been very lucky not to have sustained a more serious injury. It hadn't affected his gift of the gab, however, and Jock had been having a fine time flirting with every female in the department.

Even Sophia had been included in Jock's harmless banter.

Grace had completed two more staples when Ellen opened her mouth. 'That's three times with Donna in the last fortnight,' she mused. 'He must really like her.'

Grace's hand faltered slightly as she flicked her eyes up into Ellen's deadpan gaze. It was too shrewd by far and Grace looked back to where she'd lined up the wound for the next staple. She depressed the stapler.

'That's unusual for him?'

Grace kept the question light but seeing him with Donna had made her skin itchy, as if there were prickles in her bloodstream, and she couldn't stop the words from tumbling out.

She knew the gossip about him. She'd like to know the truth. And Ellen was a straight shooter.

Ellen nodded. 'I've known him a long time. A week with one woman is a long-term relationship to him.'

Grace's gaze flew to Ellen's face. 'A week?' She hadn't meant it to come out as a squeak—but she was pretty sure it had anyway.

She nodded. 'Brent's always dated like it's an extreme sport.' Grace swallowed as Ellen held her gaze. 'Rumour has it he was rejected by a woman a long time ago. She ruined him for all other women.'

Grace, her hand poised above the wound, had forgotten all about the task. 'Well, he is twice divorced.'

Ellen shook her head. 'No. Before that. I know his first ex-wife, Serena, and she reckons it happened back in his uni days… You knew him back then didn't you?'

Grace dropped her gaze quickly. 'Only for a couple of years,' she prevaricated, inserting another staple.

'Such a shame,' Ellen said, 'he's such a great bloke. Great doctor. So compassionate. He must have really been something in uni.'

'Er, yes.'

Grace could feel Ellen's razor-sharp gaze heavy on the top of her head as she pictured Brent's youthful physique, stretched out naked beside her. She was pretty sure Ellen hadn't been referring to Brent's body so she suppressed the sigh that rose to her lips.

'Whoever he is, he's a blind fool if he knew you back then and didn't snap you up, lassie. If I were twenty years younger, I'd make a play for you myself.'

Ellen and Grace looked at each other above their draped patient's head. Ellen winked and Grace had to stop a bubble of laughter escaping.

'If you were twenty years younger, Jock, I might just let you.'

Jock roared with laughter. 'If I'd known that, lassie, I would have taken my hard hat off years ago.'

Ellen and Grace laughed with him. 'Okay now,' Grace said when their laughter had settled. 'Hold still, another dozen or so to do.'

Grace resumed her work, concentrating on the job at hand. *Had she ruined him for other women?* He'd certainly ruined her for other men.

No one had ever matched up to him.

'Funny thing is, though,' Ellen mused, her eyes firmly on the laceration, 'until a couple of weeks ago he'd gone a good few months without any dates. Just seemed to stop cold turkey. None of us could figure that one out at all. In fact, a friend of mine had a date with him the night he'd gone for the interview for the director's position and he rang and cancelled. Hasn't been on a date since as far as any of us know. And now Donna.'

Grace let Ellen's revelations sink in. Had their meeting up again on the day of the interview after twenty years apart caused Brent to cancel his date?

And, if so, what the hell did that mean?

Brent arrived at nine on Saturday morning. Tash had been prowling around the house for two hours and wrenched open the door even before Brent had a chance to land his first knock.

He handed over a bakery packet to Tash. 'I bought croissants,' he said.

Tash wrinkled her nose. 'Are they chocolate?'

Brent shuddered. 'Absolutely not.'

'I prefer chocolate,' she said, peering into the bag.

Brent grinned. 'I'll remember that for tomorrow.'

'Aunty Grace is just in the shower,' she said, indicating for him to enter. 'She said to feed you coffee if you arrived.'

Brent shut his eyes momentarily as images of a wet, naked Grace slipped into his brain. Water sluicing off her hair, running over her breasts, down her belly, her thighs. Soap bubbles clinging to her pale pink nipples. Or maybe they weren't pale pink any more. Maybe they'd darkened over the years?

'Brent!'

His eyes flicked open and Tash came into focus. 'Sorry. What?'

'I said, do you want coffee?'

'Yes, please,' he said, shutting the door behind him.

He was going to need a lot of coffee.

Grace stepped out of the shower, patted her face dry and then slipped on her glasses. She reached for her knee-length black satin robe, wrapped herself up and belted it firmly around her waist. She opened the bathroom window and peered out at the street view. No Brent.

She cleared the fog from the mirror and gazed at her reflection. She rubbed at her hair with a towel and finger-combed it into place, tucking it behind her ears. She patted at the lines around her eyes wishing they weren't there. But nothing distracted her from Brent's absence.

Maybe he wasn't coming today after all? Maybe he'd spent all night in bed with Donna and planned to spend all day there as well.

She sank her teeth into her bottom lip as she clamped down hard on the unproductive images that simmered through her brain and prickled beneath her skin. According to Ellen, Brent had gone a while between dates—he was probably having wild animal sex right at this minute.

A tidal wave of something very akin to jealousy washed over her and she frowned at herself.

The man could sleep with whoever he damned well wanted— it was none of her business.

But Tash would be very disappointed. She'd been planning her bedroom redecoration since they'd moved in three weeks ago. A no-show would be potentially calamitous.

Things between Tash and herself hadn't shown any sign of improvement since the move. Grace had felt sure that having her own space, one that was truly hers—not Grace's, not her grandparents, but hers—would help. And it had certainly given Tash a focus, a project. But Tash was still keeping her at an emotional distance.

There was a coolness, a politeness, in the way her niece spoke to her. A way Tash had of excluding her from information she shared easily with Benji or the rest of the family. Hell, even with Brent. She wasn't overtly rude, she just wasn't inclusive, and Grace was left in no doubt that Tash was keeping her firmly on the outside.

The aroma of freshly brewed coffee wrapped her in a seductive embrace as she opened the bathroom door and Grace breathed the heavenly fragrance deep into her lungs. Deciding her caffeine need was more important than clothes, she went in search of a quick hit.

Grace entered the empty kitchen and poured herself a mug of coffee. She took a sip of the black liquid and sighed as she felt it hit her system. And then another smell assailed her—warm flaky pastry. She looked around for the source as her stomach growled loudly.

Her gaze fell on the nearby bakery bag. *Croissants?* Grace's pulse rate shot up. And it had nothing to do with the caffeine.

There hadn't been any croissants when she'd climbed into the shower fifteen minutes ago.

Brent?

Brent was here?

She looked down at her attire. Her old faithful robe that she'd owned for too many years to count and not a stitch on beneath. She turned to flee the kitchen but it was too late. Brent was lounging in the doorway.

'Morning.'

'Er…' she said rather inarticulately, clutching the lapels that tended to gape a little too much with one hand as she gripped the coffee mug hard with the other.

The man looked good enough to eat. All casual and relaxed in jeans and an old T-shirt that stretched over a taut chest and flat belly. Her innards did a strange flip-flop at his magnificence. His gaze, zeroing in on all the places where the robe clung, made her feel even more naked.

'I'm sorry…' she said, feeling at a distinct disadvantage. 'I didn't realise you were here.'

Brent nodded. That much was obvious. He opened his mouth to say words to that effect but coherent thought was difficult when her breasts were perfectly moulded by black satin and her nipples were hardening before his very eyes.

She was naked beneath the gown. *Very naked.*

A stray bead of water trekked from her hair down the side of her neck, inexorably heading for her collar bone. Every fibre of his being wanted to lick it.

'You're wearing my robe.'

It took a moment for Grace to comprehend his words. She looked down at the clothing in question, her brain slow to compute. And then it dawned on her. It *was* his gown. She'd claimed it years before, loving its silky coolness and how it had smelled just like him.

She'd kept it after they'd split. Her one tangible reminder of him. She hadn't washed it for weeks afterwards, greedily hoarding the ingrained aroma of him.

How could she have forgotten that?

'Oh…yes.' She shrugged. 'I'd forgotten.'

Brent lowered his eyes. *He hadn't.* He could see the juncture of her thighs clearly outlined by the clinging satin and he shoved his shoulder harder into the doorjamb as the urge to cover the distance between them built like a thunderstorm with every erratic thump of his heart.

How often had he peeled that damn thing off her? Slipped his fingers under the hem and stroked right where the satin now dipped to form an intriguing channel between her thighs?

He returned his gaze to her face. 'It still looks way better on you than it did on me.'

Their gazes locked. Grace didn't know what to say. He used

to whisper those words just prior to pulling the cord at her waist and sliding his hands inside.

It looks better on you than on me.

Luckily, at that moment her stomach let out an enormous rumble that could have possibly registered on a Richter scale somewhere. Grace pressed her palm against the noisy organ.

'Sorry.' She blushed. 'I'm starving.'

Brent chuckled despite the fact that her hand was no longer holding her lapels together and a tempting view of creamy cleavage was now on display.

He really had to stop ogling her like a horny teenager. She wasn't his to ogle.

They weren't together any more.

He inclined his head in the direction of the kitchen table to indicate the offerings. 'I bought croissants.'

Grace followed his gaze. 'My favourite,' she murmured.

Brent nodded and looked back at her. 'I remember.'

Grace sucked in a breath at the intensity of his tawny gaze. She remembered too. Croissants in bed from the bakery near campus. Brent deliberately using her naked body as a table, leaning over her as he sank his teeth into the moist flakiness and then slowly licking the flakes off her after he'd finished.

She returning the favour.

She'd eaten so many pastries in those days it was a wonder she wasn't as big as a house.

The phone rang and Grace almost leapt out of her skin. Tash yelled, 'I'll get it!' as she thundered down the hallway.

It was exactly what she'd needed. Grace straightened immediately. 'Ah...I'd better get dressed.' She pushed off the kitchen bench, coffee mug and lapels firmly in hand.

Brent stood aside as much as the doorway allowed, stuffing his hands into his pockets as she slipped past him. He would not reach for her. Not stop her and turn her and back her against the doorjamb and kiss her and slide his hands beneath her robe.

His robe.

It didn't matter that she smelled liked soap and shampoo and black satin. And about a thousand memories.

He knew from bitter experience that down that road lay no good.

Despite their rather shaky start the day progressed without further incident. The fact that Grace was dressed in a pair of tatty old jeans, almost completely enveloped by a huge, shapeless, paint-stained workman's shirt, definitely helped. Thank goodness for her father's cast-offs and that her mother never threw anything out.

The division of labour also helped. Tash had taken command and Grace had been relegated to helping Benji with his room while Tash shamelessly monopolised Brent.

Not that it bothered Grace. After this morning's awkwardness, it was probably best to not be in each other's pockets and it was good to spend time with Benji. She seemed to spend so much time dealing with, and worrying about, Tash that it was nice to hang out with her nephew.

He was so low maintenance compared to his sister that it was easy to forget that he was also bereaved. If it wasn't for the nightmares, Benji's suffering could easily go unnoticed.

They chatted about school. He bombarded her with facts about the gold-rush era, their current unit of learning, and chatted excitedly about the camp that was being held at the end of the year. She found out that his teacher, Miss Sykes, was allergic to strawberries and how Mr Riley from the next-door classroom yelled all day.

It was a very pleasant morning indeed. Between she and Benji bonding and the low murmur of voices she could make out from Tash's room, Grace actually felt optimistic. It was especially good to hear Tash chatting away. It was nice hearing her be natural and not stilted and guarded, as she so often was around her.

Brent popped his head into Benji's room around lunchtime to let her know that he and Tash were going to the hardware store to hire a wallpaper steamer as the current revolting wallpaper was just one of several hideous layers and that they'd bring something back for lunch.

'I think Dad has one somewhere. He did offer it so you might like to pop in there first,' she said, barely looking up from the scraping she was doing.

Brent nodded at her back. The oversized shirt had fallen off her shoulder to reveal a black bra strap and an image of her breasts encased in black satin rushed out at him.

He shook his head. The sack she was wearing should have been guaranteed to stop lustful thoughts. It didn't.

'Come on, Tash,' he said, turning away.

Grace and Benji continued. She actually found the repetitive, laborious process quite therapeutic. There was something satisfying about scraping walls. Watching the outer skin peel off in satisfying sheets, revealing the true wall beneath, the one that had been there since the house had been built.

She wished she could do the same to Tash as easily. Peel away her anger and find the grieving girl beneath.

Another flake of cartoon superman wallpaper fell victim to her scraper and Grace was pleased she'd refused the offers of help from her family. She and the kids had needed something to make this place theirs and doing it together was a step in the right direction.

Besides, Saturdays were always bedlam with the extended Perry clan when the various progeny were shuffled from one sporting or extra-curricular activity to the other. And her father, who had retired a few years ago, played golf with some friends every Saturday.

Her siblings and parents already did so much for her, helping out with the kids—she was adamant they could scrape a little wallpaper and manage a bit of painting themselves. Her father had been sceptical about her abilities but when Tash had said that Brent was helping, he'd acquiesced.

Grace should have been annoyed over the inherent sexism—like her father didn't know already she could do anything she set her mind on—but she was too grateful for his sudden about-face that she let sleeping dogs lie.

Brent arrived back an hour later with the steamer and a platter of fresh sandwiches that would feed an army. Her mother had insisted he take them. Grace bit into an egg and lettuce one and was grateful that her mother had paid no heed to Grace's protests about managing by herself.

Sandwiches on fresh white bread were just what they all needed.

They ate lunch at the kitchen table, chatting about neutral subjects. Grace watched Brent surreptitiously as he talked with the kids. Even though Tash and Benji were seven years apart in age he seemed to be able to effortlessly adjust his interaction so he was right at their levels. He joked with them and they seemed to genuinely enjoy his company.

She remembered how he'd picked up Linda's grizzling baby just a few days ago and had seemed to know instantly what would work with her. How to calm and engage her.

He was like some kind of child whisperer!

She didn't like how it made her feel. How it made her doubt the choices she'd made all those years ago. Sitting here around a table with the kids and Brent, she'd started to wonder if she'd been wrong back then. Maybe she could have had it all? Brent, kids, a career.

The irony slapped her sharply in the face. She'd turned her back on Brent because she hadn't wanted the same things he had. And yet here she was, twenty years later, with exactly the things she'd avoided.

The only difference was she was doing it alone. Without him.

Was the universe punishing her?

The conversation drifted to sport and Benji, Tash and Brent had an animated conversation about their beloved Aussie Rules team, Collingwood. 'Are you playing on a team, Benji?' Brent asked.

Benji shook his head. 'I did in Brisbane but the season was

half-over when we got back to Melbourne so I can't join the local club till next year.'

Brent could have been blind and deaf and he still would have picked up on Benji's disappointment. Not that he could blame the child. He remembered his own youth and how a game of football had been one of the few things that had been able to completely take his mind off all his problems.

What wouldn't he have given to have had enough continuity of care to play full time? To have had a father figure to kick a ball around with, to go down to the MCG and watch a game together.

In a lot of ways, he and Benji were similar and the boy's obvious disappointment resonated deeply.

A boy needed his footy. And Grace had never been a fan.

He glanced at Grace then back at Benji. 'If it's okay by your aunty, you could join the team I coach.'

Grace's eyes met Brent's. *Where had that come from?*

Benji jiggled in his seat, his eyes growing as large as soccer balls. 'You coach a team?'

Brent dragged his gaze from hers and nodded at Benji. 'It's not a club or anything. Just a bunch of kids at a local oval. We train together Sunday mornings and then play a game. You can come and see if you like it tomorrow morning.'

'Wow!' Benji bounced in his seat again and turned to face her. 'Could I, Aunty Grace, please?'

Grace could feel her nephew's excitement right down to her toes. Poor Benji, she'd tried to be both mother and father to him but she knew there were certain things that a man, a father, was better equipped to fulfil.

And football was just the beginning...

Doug and Benji had shared a passion for AFL. It wasn't until right now, with excitement radiating from Benji's eyes and vibrating through every cell of his body, that she realised how much Benji needed that connection.

For his future adjustment.

But also to help him stay connected with his past.

'I can pick him up and drop him back,' Brent prompted quietly, when a misty-eyed Grace hadn't said a word.

'Please, please, please, Aunty Grace,' Benji wheedled.

Grace smiled and blinked furiously. How could she say no? She'd been to every club in Melbourne, trying to get Benji into a team, and here was Brent offering her a perfect solution. If it pushed them together more, that was a small price to pay for Benji's happiness.

'Of course. As long as you're sure…?'

Brent nodded. 'Absolutely.'

Benji whooped, his face splitting into a huge grin. He leapt off his chair and raced around to Grace. 'Thank you, thank you, thank you,' he said, dropping a kiss on her cheek after each 'thank you'.

Grace laughed. 'Okay, okay. Don't get too excited. We've still got acres of wallpaper to go before then.'

Brent laughed too, swept up in Benji's enthusiasm. He winked at Grace and sucked in a breath as she blasted him with a one-hundred-watt dazzler.

'Okay, let's get back to work,' he said.

Before he did something insane like reach across the table and kiss that Honey Jumble smile.

CHAPTER NINE

BRENT knocked on Grace's front door at ten o'clock on Sunday morning for round two of Temptation Island. An exhilarated if somewhat muddy Benji was by his side, chatting away ten to the dozen.

To say Grace's nephew had enjoyed his morning was a massive understatement. The other kids, used to the flux nature of the team, accepted him without question and Benji, whose ball skills were impressive, had fitted right in. He was already talking about next week.

Tash answered the door again and Brent handed over another bakery bag, this time with chocolate croissants. Benji dashed off to get changed and Brent found himself hoping as he entered that Grace was not back in her baggy shirt.

She'd been in a thick woollen dressing gown that fell to her toes that morning when he'd picked Benji up and they'd had a brief thirty-second conversation. It had been a vast improvement on the short black robe.

The robe had featured in his dreams all night—elusive dreams, a mix of old memories and new fantasies—and he wasn't sure he could see her in it again and not have it off her in seconds.

He may have steeled his heart to her, shut down all possibilities other than friendship, but he *was* only flesh and blood.

He entered the kitchen to find her, hip propped against the sink, staring out the window into the back yard, a mug of coffee cradled in her hands. Denim encased her butt and hugged her legs. A spaghetti-strapped singlet-style top, covering her more than decently, clung to the hollow of her back, the slight swell of an almost flat belly and the sweet peaks of her very female chest.

Her hair was damp again and he could smell clean, soapy skin.

Oh, hell.

'Morning,' he said, propping up the doorway again.

Grace turned her head and felt the hitch in her lungs, the skip of her pulse as a slow burn ignited in her belly. She suspected she was always going to have that hitch in her breath, the catch in her pulse whenever he was near, so it was long past time she disregarded it.

The man was gorgeous.

It was just dormant chemistry.

She nodded. 'Morning. How was it?'

Brent grinned. 'Great. Benji was a hit.'

Grace smiled. 'He's a likeable kid.'

'He wants to join. I told him he'd have to okay it with you first.'

'It's fine by me as long as you're sure…'

'Of course,' he said. 'The more the merrier.'

Grace took a sip to hide the rush of gratitude as it trembled through her fingers. 'Thanks, Brent. He's rapt. It means a lot to him…to me… There are some days when not having a Y chromosome puts me at a distinct disadvantage.'

He wanted to say that from where he was standing her chromosomes were put together just right, but he shrugged instead. 'What are friends for?' he murmured, as much to remind himself as her.

Their gazes locked for a moment that seemed to drag interminably. Then Tash entered the kitchen.

'Croissants,' she announced, throwing the packet on the table and dragging out a chair. 'Chocolate.'

Grace couldn't think of anything she felt like doing less than eating but she was grateful for the interruption. 'Coffee?' she said to Brent, pouring him one without waiting for an answer.

They sat for a while, eating croissants and drinking coffee while Benji regaled them with his antics on the footy field. Grace concentrated hard on every detail, determined to ignore the fact that Brent was sitting next to her all big and warm and solid.

His laughter brushed down her side and the low sexy rumble of his voice stroked all those places his hands, his mouth knew so well.

Tash finished the last croissant and Grace leapt to her feet. 'Right, let's get this show on the road.'

After a combined effort by the four of them they'd finished scraping the multiple layers of wallpaper off Tash's room by eight o'clock last night. And both rooms stood ready for two coats of paint.

Grace escaped to her room for a mental breather before joining Benji. She needed a moment to bring her hormones under control. Being in close proximity to the man she'd once loved had been more difficult than she'd imagined. Especially when he still looked as fine as Brent did.

She really needed to get a grip!

When Brent tracked her down ten minutes later she was donning her baggy shirt. He caught sight of bare belly as Grace's singlet rode up with the action of pulling the shirt over her head.

He swallowed hard.

'Have you got drop sheets?'

Grace, appearing from the folds of fabric, almost had a heart attack as her head whipped around to locate him. Lounging in her doorway. It took a moment for her to find her voice.

'No need. Dad's arranged for some tradie friends of his to come in next week and rip up all the carpets and polish the floorboards so you can spill as much paint as you like.'

He nodded. 'Okay.' Yet he didn't seem to be able to move from the jamb. He looked around her room. Noted the unmade bed with the tangled sheets. Had her sleep been as restless as his?

'Looks like this room could do with a make-over next,' he said as he averted his gaze from the temptation of the bed to the aged flocked wallpaper decorating—dating—the walls.

Grace shook her head. If he thought he was going to be standing in here all warm muscles and capable man then he had another think coming. She had enough ammunition for her dream life without adding *Brent the Handyman* to her repertoire.

'Low down on my list of priorities,' she said briskly, walking towards him with purpose in her stride. 'Let's get to work.'

Brent took one last look at the bed, an image of rolling her over in it firmly implanting itself into his subconscious, before retreating from the doorway. He heard the firm click of her door as he headed towards Tash's room.

The click spoke volumes. *Stay out. Don't even think about it.*

His head and heart heard it loud and clear.

If only his libido wasn't profoundly deaf.

At lunchtime Grace left Brent with the kids while she dashed down to the local hardware store to buy a couple of smaller paintbrushes to do the finicky work. The rooms had each had an undercoat and should be dry enough after lunch for their top coat.

It was a good thing too. Watching Brent make himself at home in her kitchen—opening her fridge, retrieving plates from the overhead cupboards, getting a glass of water from the tap at the sink—was a little too cosy for her liking.

It was all a little too happy families. This was her house and it was dangerous to get used to having him in it. No matter how good he looked in her kitchen. No matter how much it took her back. Nothing was the same as it had been then. She had two grieving kids who were her main priority. They needed routine and security and roots.

They needed her focused.

Grace made it back to the house in thirty minutes. She could hear the chatter coming from the kitchen and smiled as she heard Benji and Tash laughing at something Brent had said in his deep, rumbly way.

She was approaching the kitchen when Tash's 'Tell us a memory' pulled her up short.

There was a moment of silence where Grace's heart all but filled her mouth. The merest hint of longing in her niece's voice was heart-wrenching. Grace pressed herself back, her palms flat against the wall.

A spike of jealousy lanced her through the middle. *Why did Tash never ask her for a memory?*

Brent looked at the two expectant faces. He'd spent all weekend with them and they'd talked and laughed and acted like two normal kids. But under the surface they were still two children whose parents had been cruelly snatched away and they were hungry for connection.

Brent understood that hunger for connection probably better than anyone.

'I remember your mum's grade-twelve graduation.'

He smiled at them as a snapshot of Julie descending the stairs in her frock came into sharp focus. 'She wasn't really a girly girl—before she met your dad anyway... I don't think I'd ever seen her in a dress before that night.'

'How come you were there?' Benji asked, his mouth full of biscuit.

'Grace and I were babysitting. I think your grandma and grandpa were going out to dinner with some other grade-twelve parents.'

'Oh, that's right,' he said, cramming another biscuit in his mouth in a display the cookie monster would have been proud of. 'I keep forgetting you used to be Aunty Grace's boyfriend.'

Brent nodded absently, wishing he could. Wishing the memories from that day hadn't stirred all the other memories.

'Was she beautiful?'

Grace heard the catch in Tash's voice and tears misted her eyes. She turned and walked the two paces to the open doorway in time to hear Brent say, 'She was gorgeous. She had on this purple floaty dress and your Aunty Grace had plaited these little white flowers in her hair.'

Brent heard a noise and looked up to find Grace in the doorway, her eyes shimmering with moisture. She looked like she was about to break.

Unbreakable Grace.

It was unbearable.

'She was so excited, wasn't she, Gracie? Doug was picking her up in a limo. She almost floated down those stairs.'

Tash and Benji's faces also sought her out and she furiously blinked back tears. 'Yes.' She smiled, moving her legs automatically, feeling like a robot as she made her way to the table and sat down.

She reached her hands across the flat tabletop palms up, reaching for their hands. Benji took hers eagerly. Tash moved her hands away, placing them on her lap. Grace tried not to feel the snub all the way down to her bones.

She pulled her empty hand back and placed it over top of her and Benji's linked fingers. 'She could barely sit still. It took me ages to weave those flowers through her hair.'

Brent saw the emotional flinch as Tash's silent rejection hit Grace hard. He'd hoped by including Grace in the memory that Tash might open up a little towards her aunt.

Apparently not.

He wanted to place his hand on top of Grace's, give it a squeeze, but it was important that he didn't allow even the slightest chink in his heart.

The chink in his libido was bad enough.

'What was that flower called?' he asked.

Grace bit hard on her lip at the memory of the tiny white buds. 'Baby's breath.'

'Baby's breath?' Benji asked, pushing his chair back and not waiting for a reply as he raced out of the room.

They barely had time to blink before he was back again, carrying the photo frame that sat on Grace's dressing table. Benji had asked her ages ago what the flowers in his mother's hair were called.

'Is this from then?' he asked, thrusting it at Brent.

It was a snap from that night. Julie, all dolled up, grinning madly at the camera, with her arm slung over Grace's shoulder. Grace also laughing into the camera. Happy for her sister. And madly in love with the photographer.

Brent nodded, his thumb sweeping along the thick ceramic border. 'I took that photo.'

'Really?' Benji did an excited little jump. 'Isn't that amazing, Tash?' Benji said, shoving the photo at his sister. 'Brent took this picture all those years ago.'

Grace watched as Tash looked at the picture. For a moment Grace thought her niece was going to burst into tears and then her mouth tightened and she looked up like nothing in the world was bothering her.

'It's a small world, Benji boy,' she said, ruffling her brother's hair, avoiding the two adult gazes. 'Now, come on.' She stood and started clearing the table. 'We've got another coat of paint to do.'

Brent raised an enquiring eyebrow at Grace as Tash retreated to the sink. Grace shrugged. It was no use asking her—she didn't know what went on inside her niece's head any more.

By seven o'clock both rooms' paint jobs had been completed. Tash now had three bright purple walls and one burnt orange one that somehow seemed to work. All Benji's walls were one colour—mint green with darker green trim.

They looked fresh and modern and a far cry from the wallpapered monstrosities of two days ago.

Brent was cleaning the brushes in the laundry when Grace tracked him down. 'We're getting pizza—are you in?'

Brent looked up from his task. She'd taken off her baggy shirt and was back to the singlet top. She looked so damn sexy standing in the doorway looking at him, hand on hip, through her black-rimmed glasses, her feet bare, her short, shaggy hair framing her face. Her Honey Jumble lips glistened in the half-light.

Frankly she was a sight for sore eyes.

He was tired from two days of physical labour—his neck and shoulder muscles ached—and a fitful night's sleep.

He didn't feel like being her friend tonight. His resistance was at a very low ebb.

'You don't have to feed me,' he said, returning his attention to the brushes.

'It's the least we can do,' she dismissed. 'Besides, the kids won't be impressed with me if I just let you run off home.'

She smiled, trying to keep it light, but she knew that Tash and Benji had just assumed he would be joining them and she didn't want to disappoint them.

Brent closed his eyes for a second, fighting the urge to turn off the taps, take two strides towards her and yank her into his arms.

She frowned at his hesitation and then it dawned on her. 'Oh, sorry.' She raised her palm to her forehead. 'You've got a date…' She dropped her hand to her side. 'Look, don't worry, the kids will understand… Please, you've already done enough this weekend—'

'Grace!' He didn't mean it to come out as forcefully as it did but her assumption had rankled. Apart from a few recent dates with Donna, which had been more for distraction than anything else, he hadn't dated since Grace had barged back into his life.

He couldn't even remember the last time he'd had sex.

'I *do not* have a date. Thank you, I would love to eat with you. And Tash and Benji,' he quickly clarified. He patted his belly. 'I'm starving, actually.'

Grace's gaze dropped to where his hand rested against his flat stomach. The sudden urge to see it again assailed her and she gripped the doorjamb hard in case her hands decided to follow through.

Perhaps Brent staying for dinner wasn't such a wise idea after all...

'Good. I'll go and order, then.'

Half an hour later they were all spread out in the lounge room in front of the television, shovelling pizza into their mouths and watching the Sunday football game that Benji had recorded.

The kids had taken a single lounge each, leaving the triple-seater for Grace. Brent had chosen the floor, propping his back against the three-seater a respectable distance from Grace.

It didn't mean that he wasn't excruciatingly aware of her denim-clad thighs in his peripheral vision or of every single movement she made. Or that the lounge wasn't big enough to stretch out, push her back and reacquaint himself with her body.

But she was out of reaching distance. All he had to do was eat, drink and keep his gaze locked on the television.

'Oh, no,' Benji groaned just prior to half-time when the referee called a penalty against his beloved Collingwood. 'The Cats were offside, not us,' he called to the television.

Brent took a deep swallow of his beer. 'I think the ref needs glasses, mate,' he said to Benji.

'Maybe he can borrow Aunty Grace's.' Benji laughed.

Brent joined in. 'I don't think they'd suit him.'

Grace smiled. She was pleased that Brent had agreed to stay. Her interest in and knowledge of football was minimal but as both kids were dyed-in-the-wool AFL fans, she'd been making an effort.

And now, like it or lump it, she was also a Collingwood supporter.

Brent missed the next goal as Grace shifted in the chair, tucking her left foot up under her right knee. Her breasts bounced enticingly with the move and he took another deep swallow of his beer.

'I'm taking the kids from the footy team to the match next weekend,' he said, desperate to distract himself. 'Would you guys like to come?'

Tash and Benji looked at him like he'd just bought the Collingwood football team for them. 'Seriously?' Tash demanded.

'Really?' Benji asked.

Brent chuckled. 'Really. Seriously. Even your aunt can come.'

Benji turned pleading eyes on his aunt, his little hands clasped together. 'Oh, can we, Aunty Grace? I know you don't like football, but can we? Can we, can we, can we?'

Grace laughed. 'Ah, yeah, I guess.' She looked at Brent. 'Are you sure?'

Sure? No. But at least he'd have a whole bunch of kids to distract him. And nowhere handy to lay her down.

An hour later the game had ended and Grace rounded up two unprotesting kids. Not even Tash gave her grief about going to bed at eight-thirty. They said goodnight to Brent and Grace herded them into her bedroom.

The paint fumes in their own rooms were still a little too toxic for safe sleeping so they were spending the night with her. With both bedroom windows open and fans on low, the fumes should be non-existent by the morning.

'I'll lie with Benji until he goes to sleep,' Tash said, climbing in next to her brother. 'Then I'll sleep on the mattress.'

Grace looked at Tash's mattress, which was made up on the floor next to her bed. 'You can sleep with me too,' she said. 'The bed's big enough. You'll probably be more comfortable.'

Tash stiffened and shook her head. 'No, thank you.'

Grace felt the icy blast from her polite rejection deep inside and steeled herself not to react. 'Okay.' She nodded. 'No probs.'

Still, feelings of alienation shadowed her as she walked back to the empty lounge room and she hugged herself. Brent entered from the kitchen, juggling two full rubbish bags, several empty pizza boxes and his keys.

'I'll be off too,' he said, not giving himself time to think or feel or analyse why the hell he was getting out of this house—fast. 'I'll dump these in the wheelie bin on the way out.'

Grace nodded. 'Here,' she said, relieving him of the boxes. 'I'll give you a hand.'

She followed him out the front door, her mind still preoccupied with Tash. The coolness of the night air didn't register, not even the way Brent's denim-clad butt strutted in front of her registered.

They dumped their cargo in the bins that lived beside the garage and Brent headed for his car parked in the driveway. He pressed the unlock button on his key and four lights flashed momentarily, illuminating the relative darkness.

He stopped by his door. 'Well, I guess I'll see you at work. When are you on next?' he asked.

Grace, still preoccupied with Tash, had to think for a moment. 'Tuesday.'

Brent nodded. His heart was thumping in his chest like a teenager on a first date trying to work up the courage to steal a kiss.

He was not going to kiss her.

He pulled the handle and the door opened. 'Until Tuesday, then.'

The soft snick of the door opening pulled Grace out of her reverie. Where were her manners? 'I'm sorry,' she apologised. 'I'm a little distracted.'

A little distracted? Brent almost groaned out loud as she propped her hip against the back passenger door and vanilla wafted towards him from her Honey Jumble mouth.

He was very distracted.

'I don't know how to thank you for the last couple of days. The job would have been a lot slower without you, and the kids have really enjoyed your company. You've really clicked with

Tash, and inviting Benji to join your footy team was the icing on the cake.'

Brent knew exactly how she could thank him. *It involved hands and mouths and lots and lots of naked skin.*

Grace looked up at him, all solid and warm in front of her, but the streetlight was behind him, cloaking his eyes in darkness, and she couldn't read his expression. Still, the urge to unburden was overwhelming.

Just like old times.

'You're so good with them.'

Brent heard a trace of anguish in her voice. *Damn.* 'You're good with them too.'

Grace desperately wanted to believe but she knew it wasn't true. She shook her head. 'No, I'm not. Benji, sure, but Tash…' Grace grasped her upper arms as the cool night air finally began to register. 'I don't know about that…'

Brent gripped his door harder. *Please don't do this.* Please don't look at me with big, lost eyes. 'She's been through a lot—'

'No,' Grace interrupted earnestly, taking a step towards him. 'It's more than that—she's angry.'

'Her parents died, Grace.'

Grace shook her head and moved closer still. 'No. Not at that. At me. She's angry with me for some reason.'

Brent didn't know what to say, what to tell her. She was so close. When he breathed in, his lungs filled with her. Every rational thought flew from his head as the desire to pull her into his arms and kiss her until all the anguish went away consumed him.

Grace shook her head as his growing silence brought her out of herself. 'I'm sorry.' She took a step back and rubbed at her arms. 'I'm keeping you.' She might not have been able to see his eyes but she could sense his reluctance to be there.

Like he couldn't wait to get away.

Well, duh! Just because he'd said he didn't have a date it

didn't mean he wasn't hooking up with someone later. Maybe he was up for a booty call somewhere?

'Go. You go,' she said, rubbing at her arms more vigorously, suddenly feeling cold on the inside as well. Cold down to her bones.

Oh, hell. 'You're cold,' he said.

And then he stepped closer to her, knocking her hands aside as he took over the job. Her skin was cool. But as soft and smooth as he remembered. 'You should have a jumper on,' he chided, as each pass of his hands wafted more of her sweet aroma towards him.

Grace felt his brisk, completely impersonal touch fan across her pelvic floor muscles. Her nipples tightened and she tried to tell herself it was the cold but she knew it was a lie.

'I'm sorry,' she whispered, because she couldn't think of anything else to say.

Brent looked down into her face. Light from the streetlight slanted across her cheekbones, illuminating her glistening, slightly parted lips. And the confusion in her grey eyes.

His hands stilled on her upper arms.

'Oh, hell,' he muttered, as the last of his resistance melted away and he pulled her towards him, his mouth swooping down to cover hers.

CHAPTER TEN

GRACE went to him willingly. He was so big and solid and warm, and in ten seconds flat she was hot. Hot all over.

For his touch. For his kiss. For him.

She groaned against his mouth as his palms slid up her neck and cradled her jaw, locking her head in place as his tongue plunged inside her mouth. She bunched his T-shirt in her hand, pulling him closer, needing him nearer.

Brent turned, pushed her back against the car door, swallowing her gasp as the tastes of Grace—honey and vanilla—filled him up. He opened his mouth wider, pushed his tongue deeper, wanting more of her taste, needing more.

Grace felt the cold metal of the passenger door brand like fingers of arctic ice on her fevered skin. There was fever in her blood as well, licking like flame through her body, flushing heat over her skin and scorching her insides.

Her nipples, already unbearably erect, tightened further. Her belly contracted. Her thighs quivered. A tingling between her legs intensified until it itched and burned and she rubbed herself against him, against his hardness, to relieve it.

Brent dug his fingers into her hips as her frustrated growl and agitated grinding against his aching erection drove him a little closer to insanity. He wanted more.

To be horizontal.

To be over her.

In her.

To look down at her as she came.

He dragged his mouth from hers, pulling her off the cold

metal as he reached for the car door. 'In,' he gasped, as the door opened and he manoeuvred her backwards.

Grace didn't argue, somehow managing to back into the back seat without injuring herself and pull him in with her too. She drew up her knee and let it fall against the seat. Placed her other foot in the footwell, opening her denim-clad legs wide, forming a perfect cradle for his hips.

The back of his sporty convertible was cramped and the cold night air was pushing inside from the open door where both of Brent's legs hung out. But his weight was pressing her into the seat and his mouth was back on hers and nothing else mattered.

She grabbed a handful of his T-shirt where it covered his shoulder and tugged, ruching it up and dragging it over his head. Her greedy hands revelled in the solid warm muscles of his back as she kissed his jaw and his neck and his collar bone. Then his greedy mouth demanded her attention again.

Brent couldn't get enough of her mouth. Every sweet curve held a memory and he wanted to plunder them until he'd remembered every one. But her nails dragged down his back, dug into his backside, slipped under his waistband and squeezed his bare buttocks, and kissing her mouth was no longer enough.

He wanted to kiss her everywhere. Lick all the places that made her shiver.

Taste her.

His hand reached for her singlet top and pushed it up. His palm felt the ridges of her ribs and then his fingers touched the edge of cushioned satin. She moaned as his hand moved to claim all of her breast and his thumb flicked over her taut nipple.

He dragged his mouth from hers, ignoring her hoarse whimper. He needed to taste the tight little berry grazing his fingertips. Lave it with his tongue, suck on it until it grew large and engorged in his mouth.

He yanked her bra cup aside, remembering how sensitive

her breasts had been, how crazy it had made her when he'd worshipped them.

Grace bucked against him, biting her lip to prevent the expletive as Brent's hot tongue swiped across her tortured nipple. She dug her fingers into his shoulders and arched her back.

How had she ever erased this from her mind? This bliss that he created. This erotic havoc that scrambled her brain and turned her into a pleasure-seeking android with no question of sense or protest or denial.

He pulled her other bra cup aside and sucked that nipple straight into his hot, hot mouth. She cried out. Was it possible that he'd got even better?

What else had changed?

What else was better?

Suddenly she needed to see all of him. Touch all of him. Reconnect with what had once been very familiar territory.

Hoping she had enough functioning brain cells left while Brent continued to lave her breasts with his tongue, she reached between their bodies for his fly. Her hand brushed the bulge beneath and her fingers shook in anticipation.

She breached his zipper and underpants within seconds and a guttural sound of triumph escaped her lips as she wound her fingers around his thickness. It filled her palm, just as she remembered, and she ran her hand up and down its length.

Brent reared back as sensation ripped through his groin and spasmed through his buttocks and belly. He felt as if he'd been struck by lightning and he released her nipple as a deep groan tore from his mouth.

His whole body bucked. His head hit the armrest and his shin banged hard against the metal framework of the door.

It was just the dose of reality he needed.

What the hell was he doing? Making out in a car with Grace like a horny teenager while her sister's bereaved kids were asleep in the house.

Grace, who hadn't wanted him twenty years ago and certainly didn't have time for him in her life now.

Other than a quickie in the back of a car.

'Are you okay?' she whispered stroking her hand against him again. Once, twice, three times.

Brent fought the urge to let his eyes roll back in his head, to push himself further into her palm, to rock his hips.

'Wait,' he said. 'Just wait.'

He placed his forehead on her chest, trying to think over the roar of his pulse and the gasp of his breath as he fought to get more oxygen into his lungs.

Grace, still dazed and foggy, her own pulse loud in her ears, her breath ragged, struggled to understand his command.

Wait?

She fought the whimper that rose in her throat.

What? No. She moved her hand again.

Brent squeezed his eyes shut tight. 'No.' He angled his hips away, dislodging her hand, breathing hard into her chest.

They lay there for a moment or two longer before Brent eased back, bending his knees then lifting himself off her. Grace, stunned at the sudden turnaround, fixed her bra, pulled her shirt down, drew her legs up and swung them round until she was sitting where moments ago her head had been.

She ran a shaky hand through her hair as Brent sat on the seat next to her and retrieved his shirt from the floor. Her face was still flushed, hot. She was still burning up, still hot for him everywhere.

'I'm sorry,' he said as he pulled his shirt back over his head.

Grace dragged in a breath. 'It's fine.'

Brent raked a hand through his hair. 'I can't...do this with you again.'

Grace felt her second rejection tonight like a sledgehammer to her heart. Even though she knew he was right. Knew stopping what had just happened had been the best move. Even if her body did feel like it had been denied something she'd been craving for twenty years.

'I know.'

Damn it, why was she being so bloody reasonable when he wanted to smash things? They could have been doing this for the last twenty years. They'd had something good and she'd ruined it.

'You can't just waltz back into my life and expect to pick up where we left off, Grace.' He wasn't sure if he was saying it for her benefit or for his.

She placed her forehead against the seat back. 'I don't.'

Brent glanced at her sharply. 'Yeah, well, it sure didn't feel like it just now.'

'Hey.' Her head snapped up and she glared at him. 'You kissed me.'

Brent glared back, his breath sawing in and out of her lungs. She was right. He was angrier with himself than with her. It was just easier to blame her than take responsibility.

He sighed, throwing himself back against the car seat. 'I'm sorry. I'm just...I hate how you still get under my skin. I wish I still didn't...want you so much.'

Grace felt her anger deflate just as quickly. 'Same here,' she murmured. 'But we've got a lot of history. It's to be expected, I guess.'

They sat for a moment or two in silence, each contemplating the enormity of the admissions they'd made tonight. It wouldn't make it go away but it might make it easier between them.

Grace turned, her hand on the doorhandle. 'See you next week.'

'Can you just answer me one question?' he asked.

Grace paused, one leg out of the car. 'Sure.'

Brent leaned forward, his elbows on his knees, his hands in his hair. 'Why did you agree to marry me? Why say yes, why put my ring on your finger only to break it off two months later? I don't believe it was ever about me distracting you from your studies. What's the truth, Grace?'

Grace felt her heart slow for a moment before it kicked back in with a painful thump. 'Because I loved you, Brent, and you wanted it so much. I wanted to make you happy.'

'Sounds like good reasons to stay together.'

'But I didn't want what you wanted. I didn't want babies and the whole white-picket-fence thing. I wanted to be a doctor, I wanted a career.'

'I told you I didn't need that.'

Grace gripped the handle hard. 'Yes, but I knew you wanted it. And I knew you'd be miserable without it. You'd had a miserable childhood and it was your time to be happy, Brent. I wouldn't have made you happy.'

'There's more than that, Grace. There has to be.'

Grace nodded. He was right. She'd never told him before because it had always seemed so selfish, but maybe she owed it to him now. 'I was afraid I'd give in to you because I loved you too much. And then I'd have been miserable.'

And there was more but she just couldn't say it out loud. *I was afraid that I loved you so much that I'd start to want it all too. That I'd give up my dreams without blinking an eyelid.*

Brent dropped his hands and turned to look at her. 'And we're both so happy now, right?'

The irony was not lost on Grace. They were both living a life neither of them had wanted. The only difference was that they were doing it without each other.

But what was done was done.

'See you Tuesday,' she said, climbing out of the car and shutting the door after her.

Grace headed straight for the shower, stripping off her clothes, plunging herself beneath the spray, trying to wash away his smell, his touch, his taste. Her body still craved them but deep in her soul she knew she had to expel every last trace of him from her body.

Or lie awake all night, going slowly mad.

As the water drummed against her face his words repeated themselves over and over. *You can't just waltz back and pick up where we left off.* She let it replay. Let it chase round and round her head on continuous loop. Because she needed to remember. She needed her body to remember.

They weren't together any more.

Things between them were still complicated. Different complicated sure, but complicated nonetheless. And she would not allow herself to mess up a relationship with him the second time around because of some misplaced sense of nostalgia. Or latent chemistry.

They weren't together any more.

After a couple of minutes Grace shut off the taps briskly, shutting off the voices in her head just as decisively.

She got it. *They weren't together any more.*

She dried herself briskly. Time to start thinking about what she did have, the here and now, not the things she couldn't have.

The kids, her home, her family.

Her job.

She wondered, as she headed to her bedroom, when medicine had become such an afterthought.

The answer greeted her as she crossed the threshold to her room. Tash and Benji lying in her bed, sound asleep. Her troubled thoughts ceased as her heart filled with love for these two bereaved kids. They looked so sweet and innocent like this—how could life be so cruel?

They were her priority now. Everything else was secondary.

Still, despite lecturing herself about priorities, Grace spent the next few days obsessing over the back-seat incident. Reliving it *ad nauseam.* Wondering how it might have ended if Brent hadn't put the brakes on. Alternating between embarrassment at their teenage behaviour and supreme sexual frustration.

And as Tuesday inched closer she grew more and more nervous about what they'd say to each other. About how it would be between them.

She needn't have worried.

Tuesday started with a bang and didn't get any better. There certainly wasn't any time for psychoanalysis.

Her sister Wendy rang at about seven-thirty as Grace was packing the kids' lunches to let Grace know that her daughter, Kelly, had seen Tash and some other girls hanging around a local park smoking after school the previous day.

Grace confronted Tash. An argument ensued. Grace struggled to keep her cool—Tash felt no such compunction. She loudly denied it as Grace snatched her niece's bag from her and searched it for contraband. She found nothing but she could detect a faint trace of tobacco and she confiscated Tash's iPod and grounded her for a fortnight.

Tash slammed out of the house, tears streaming down her face, yelling about living in a prison.

And then at work there was no time for awkwardness or talking the situation to death. Grace had barely been at work for an hour when the hospital was plunged into chaos.

A light aeroplane had crashed onto a nearby high school oval, ploughing into the crowds that had had been enjoying their annual sports carnival. Both Melbourne Central, the Royal Melbourne and the Children's Hospital had activated their external disaster plans and were expecting mass casualties.

After an initial gut-wrenching moment when Grace had to be reassured that it wasn't Tash's high school, she clicked into her doctor zone. She'd been involved in many mock disasters in her time and knew the routine back to front.

To be able to deal with situations like this, hospitals—emergency departments particularly—had extensive protocols in place. Planning and practice for such incidents was a must and all hospital departments trained for this kind of eventuality.

She knew the Central would be no different.

Brent assured her that the hospital maintained a high state of preparedness for this kind of situation and had the staff, the skills and the capacity to cope.

External disasters also required leadership, communication and collaboration with all emergency services—police, fire and ambulance. When Brent received the request from the field command to send two senior doctors and nursing staff to the scene to help with triage, he didn't hesitate in calling on Grace.

'Let's go,' he said, their necking session in the back seat of his car on Saturday night unimportant in the face of the potentially dire situation not two kilometres from their doorstep. 'They need us for triage.'

Grace nodded. 'Everything's ready to go here. ICU and OT are on standby. All wards and medical teams have been notified. We have a dozen registrars and Ellen has arranged to pull extra nursing staff from the wards.'

'Good.' He nodded. 'We'll grab her and two other nurses as well.'

Ten minutes later they were all piling out of Brent's car at the accident scene. They were dressed in navy-blue overalls and laden with equipment. Grace and Brent had *Doctor* emblazoned front and back. The nurses' overalls were marked *Nurse*.

Grace's nostrils flared at the pungent smell of burning Avgas as she took in the carnage. The oval looked as if it was a scene from a post-apocalyptic movie. People milled everywhere as they were directed to medical stations. Some crying, some shouting, others bloodied and obviously injured or looking frantically for others.

Emergency services vehicles were parked haphazardly all round the oval—fire trucks, police cars and ambulances. They looked like toy cars amidst the enormous scale of the destruction. Sirens pealed everywhere—in the distance and nearby. News helicopters swarmed overhead.

Black smoke rose from the smouldering remains of what she assumed was the aircraft. It was being continually doused by a team of firemen. It seemed to have torn up half of the oval, scorching the earth in its wake as well as upending various stands, ploughing into a packed wooden grandstand, collapsing it and setting it alight.

'Let's report to the central command post,' Brent said, rousing them all out of their momentary stupor.

The officer in charge, Dr Jennifer Warner, was pleased to see them. 'Most of the triage is complete. The casualties have been grouped in red, green and yellow.'

She pointed to the make shift 'stations' where people either sat or lay.

'We have seven black tags over there. Two students. Five adults. That doesn't include the pilot, who is presumed dead.'

She indicated with her thumb over her shoulder to the deceased, who were covered in sheets. Two police officers were constructing a canvas screen to block the morbid sight from the eyes in the sky and the gathering press contingent that were like hounds baying for blood behind the police tape cordon that had been erected to keep non-emergency personnel out of the area.

Grace shivered. Seven dead. Plus the pilot. She glanced back at the twisted, charred shell. Surely no one could have survived that impact?

'Could you all head towards the red tags and get as many treated and transported as possible?'

'On it,' Brent said.

And then it was all go, go, go.

Grace knew as she headed into the fray that all the victims sporting red tags around their wrists would have been assessed as requiring immediate medical attention because they had life-threatening injuries. If they had difficulty breathing, lacked a radial pulse, were in shock or unable to follow simple commands, they would have been tagged as red.

As they pushed through the crowds of dazed people Grace noticed many of them were being ushered to the green area and had green tags dangling from their wrists. They were essentially the walking wounded who had suffered minor injuries only and wouldn't be seen until after the high-priority casualties had been evacuated.

Just before reaching the red area they passed the yellow

station, which seemed inundated with victims. A yellow tag indicated injuries that were not fatal or life-threatening. These people would have a good pulse and would be able to follow simple commands, but couldn't sit or stand because of injuries.

Grace knew that these patients, though not requiring immediate attention, would need treatment within the next few hours.

It was going to be a long day.

'Doc, here!' A paramedic indicated frantically at them and it was all hands on deck.

Grace didn't know how many people she treated in that first two hours. Kneeling on the ground beside stretchers, putting in lines, controlling haemorrhages, splinting fractures. Evacuating the critical into a seemingly endless convoy of ambulances. Pulling off her gloves, snapping on a new pair and starting again with the next one.

It was automatic.

She and Brent, working side by side, the sun beating down on their heads, as if they'd been working together for the last twenty years. Royal Melbourne doctors working with them too. All being methodical and thorough. Complementing each other.

Blocking out the extraneous noise of the ebb and flow of people all around them. Adults, students who'd been on the oval walking around dazed or sobbing, comforting each other. Emergency personnel going about their jobs with grim efficiency. Panicked parents arriving at the school, frantic for their children.

Someone handed them water to drink and a chocolate bar to eat every half an hour. They gulped them down without protest and then turned their attention back to the task at hand. Treating the wounded.

'Got one for you, Doc.' A paramedic and a fireman arrived with a man on a field stretcher. 'He's just been pulled from under the grandstand. He's critical. No radial. Weak carotid. Gurgly airway. Blown left pupil.'

Brent and Grace made way for the stretcher. The patient was unconscious with a large head wound. Brent felt the faint flutter of a pulse. Grace reached for the nearby portable suction unit, opened a new Yankeur sucker and pushed it onto the end of the tubing. She inserted into the man's mouth and cleared his airway. Blood filled the tubing.

'Two minutes of CPR,' Brent said.

Grace reached for the ambu-bag and administered the breaths, the patient's chest rising and falling in sync with Brent's compressions.

At two minutes the paramedic called, 'Time.'

Brent stopped, felt for a pulse, waiting many seconds longer than was necessary. Nothing. Maybe he could have saved this man, this stranger that had been in the wrong place at the wrong time, if he'd had two hours, a neurosurgeon and a hospital full of equipment.

But he didn't.

He could, however, with any luck, save the twenty more people with red tags lined up for them on stretchers.

And that, unfortunately, was what happened in mass casualty situations. Priorities. Treating quickly and efficiently and evacuating the living to a tertiary centre. Not spending precious minutes on someone that couldn't be saved.

Brent snapped off his gloves. 'Tag him with a black and put him with the others.'

There was a brief pause amidst the activity all around them, shared by the four. Staring down into the dead man's face, Grace felt a surge of impotence as the futility of the situation overwhelmed her almost more than the pervasive smell of Avgas.

What was his name? Was he a parent? A teacher? What could he have possibly done in his life to deserve dying today in this way, surrounded by strangers?

It helped put things into perspective. Life was fragile. Grace knew she should know that better than anyone. Between her job and losing Julie. But it was easy to forget amidst the hustle and bustle of it all. It was easy to let the continuing juggle with life and problems with Tash overwhelm her.

She was all right. The kids were all right. She and Brent would be all right.

Her life wasn't perfect. It wasn't all neat and controlled, as she would have liked.

But she was doing all right. And she'd get there.

Then the guys who had brought the patient to them, whose names she also didn't know, were picking up the stretcher and carrying it away.

'Well, that sucks,' Grace said as her gaze tracked their progress.

Brent nodded, dragging his eyes from them as well to look down at her. 'You okay?'

She looked at him. 'Yep.'

And she turned to her next patient.

CHAPTER ELEVEN

ON SUNDAY Grace drove Benji to the oval with a recalcitrant Tash. Her niece was still incensed over losing her iPod and the grounding, so things were tense. Benji was oblivious but Grace's gut was churning madly.

Brent, looking all tall, dark and handsome, was a powerful antidote.

Or was that aphrodisiac?

He was wearing tatty old jeans and a Collingwood hoodie and was so sexy she wanted to tackle him to the ground and pash him in front of twenty impressionable children who obviously hero-worshipped him.

However his *You can't just waltz in and pick up where you left off* beat like little frantic bird wings in her grey matter and she just managed to bring her body under control.

Even though kissing him seemed much more preferable to talking with a stony-faced Tash. And way more pleasurable.

Half of her extended family arrived to watch Benji play, which not only swelled the spectator ranks considerably but made it easier to be around Brent.

Sort of.

It certainly gave her something else to focus on. But every word of praise from the sidelines, every whistle blow from Brent drew her gaze and dug the well of longing a little deeper.

It seemed their passionate clinch in the car had popped the cork on her repressed libido and his pure physicality on the field was stoking it ever higher.

But even more so, his interaction with the kids.

He was marvellous with them all, Benji included. He laughed

and joked. Cajoled and encouraged. Praised and advised. And he didn't mind a bit of rough-housing. More than once he stole the ball and ran with it and a dozen kids chased after him, laughing and yelling, 'Get him!' all the way.

He let them catch him and he let them tackle him to the ground and jump on him. He came up laughing and roaring, dragging as many kids clinging to his arms and legs as he could as he strode towards the goal line.

They plainly adored him.

And it was easy to see why.

When the game was over for the morning and the kids had been taken home by their foster-parents, the Perry clan decided to keep the game going. Everyone, including Grace, got dragged into the fray and much hilarity ensued. Even Tash forgot her bad mood and got into the spirit of it all.

Brent led the kids' team and Marshall led the adults. Some would have said that was unfair but the kids disagreed and Brent was their champion. Grace spent most of the time running around without a clue of what she was doing, mainly just ogling Brent as he whizzed past, throwing and kicking and diving.

He was a sight to behold.

So distracted was she that it was a complete surprise at one stage to end up with the ball. She stared at it dumbfounded for a moment. Then Benji yelled, 'Get her,' to a nearby Brent. Grace looked up as a look of pure devilish fun lit Brent's tawny gaze and he started towards her, bellowing like an Apache on the warpath.

'Run!' Marshall yelled.

Grace took one look at the mischief in Brent's gaze and didn't need to be told twice. She gave an inhuman squeak, turned and ran towards the goalposts, a cacophony of cheers and screams propelling her.

But she was no match for Brent's superior prowess and she hadn't gone far before he swooped in and bundled her up close to his chest, spinning round and round, the sky and clouds and treetops twisting and turning like the multi-hued petals of a kaleidoscope.

'Stop, Brent,' she begged, clutching the ball with one hand and his shirt with the other, hanging on for dear life, her head spinning and her side hurting from laughing harder than she had in a very long time.

'Put me down. Put me down. I'm getting dizzy.' Everything spun and moved, including her crazy silly heart, flopping in her chest like an epileptic fish.

Brent laughed, dizzy himself. 'Okay, you asked for it,' he murmured, falling to his knees and half dropping, half placing her on the ground as the earth spun. Her arms clutched at his neck as she fell backwards, pulling him down, pulling him across her.

'Oomph!' The inelegant noise escaped from Grace's mouth as Brent's big, warm body squashed hers into the cool grass.

He chuckled. 'Sorry.'

Grace laughed too. 'Mmm,' she said, shutting her eyes. 'Everything is spinning.'

Brent levered his knee between her legs and half pushed himself off her, looking down into her face, her mouth so very near. She looked so beautiful his breath became momentarily trapped in his lungs. 'I see you just fine.'

Grace opened her eyes, still smiling. And then awareness kicked in.

Of him.

Everything else faded into the background. Her family racing towards them, their claps and cheers and wild laughter. The cars on the nearby busy-for-a-Sunday road. Even the plane overhead.

Instead she could feel his heart beat beneath her palm, feel his warm breath on her cheek, hear the harsh suck of oxygen as it sawed in and out of his lungs, see the dilation of his pupils.

Brent shook his head, trying to clear the roar of the blood coursing through his ears. 'This is crazy,' he muttered.

Grace watched his mouth as it formed the words. It was so very close. 'Yes.'

She didn't need to ask him to clarify. She knew what he meant. This thing still between them *was* crazy.

And then Benji leapt onto Brent's back crying out, 'Geronimooooo!'

'Oomph,' Grace said again, as Brent and Benji's combined weight pressed down on her. The action zapped her back to the present with the startling force of a cattle prod.

Her family crowding around, reaching for them, laughing, helping them up.

The cars, the plane, the noise.

'Got it!' Tash exclaimed as she wrestled the ball from Grace's unprotesting fingers and ran with it.

Benji whooped and ran after his sister. Brent, trying and failing to compute those few cataclysmic moments pressed against Grace, dragged his gaze away from the woman in question.

'Run, kids, run,' he shouted. 'Faster,' he said, as he took off after them, needing to get away from Grace, Far, far away. She had grass in her hair and he wanted to lay her back down and kiss those Honey Jumble lips until they both forgot their names.

He ran and ran, hoping he could run away from the craziness. 'Faster,' he called, gaining on the kids and then reaching them.

Without breaking stride, he grabbed for their waists and swooped them both up, carrying them effortlessly, holding one under each arm—a teenage girl and a seven-year-old boy—like they weighed no more than footballs. Tash and Benji giggled and screamed all the way until Brent reached the goalposts and they all collapsed in a heap.

The Perry family clapped and cheered. Marshall let out an almighty whistle that would have done any sheep farmer proud. Benji, Tash and Brent all sprang up. They jumped up and down, high-fiving each other.

Grace watched with a lump in her throat as Brent put an arm

around each of the kids' shoulders and pulled them against his sides, all of them laughing.

He didn't look like an important emergency care physician, standing there, laughing with her kids.

He looked like a father.

She smiled through the lump as it grew larger, threatening to choke her as a sudden awful certainty settled into her bones.

She loved him.

She'd never stopped loving him.

Grace couldn't sleep that night. She tossed and turned, the sheets twisting around her legs, tangling her up as euphoria battled with despair. The realisation that her epiphany earlier in the day was worthless had come swiftly to her in the silence of the night.

You can't just waltz back in and pick up where you left off.

The finality, the power, of those words echoed endlessly around her head, chasing each other through the long dark hours. They vanquished any fledgling hopes of dozens of dormant fantasies that tried to rise above them.

You can't just waltz back in and pick up where you left off.

Sure, he still found her attractive, still desired her. A few magical moments in the back seat of his car and an intense moment in the park were testament to that.

They had undeniable chemistry.

But what about his heart?

Did he still love her?

Could he?

Or had he shut himself off to a second chance with her? Had she hurt him too badly? When she'd *ruined him for all women*, had she blown it for herself too?

Because after twenty years without his love she needed more than sexual attraction.

She didn't want to be just two bodies slaking a two-decade-old thirst. Although, God knew, as she balled her hand into a fist and stuffed it between her legs, she wanted to feel him inside her again so badly it was a physical ache.

Which grew fiercer by the second.

She wanted to love him.

Wanted him to let her love him.

Could she just go to him and tell him what a fool she'd been? That she'd been wrong about all the things she'd said she hadn't wanted because she had them now and the world hadn't come to an end and she still had a career.

The only thing she didn't have was him.

Could it be that simple?

You can't just waltz in and pick up where you left off.

She groaned into her pillow. She'd stuffed up—big-time.

What if he never let her back in?

She'd have to fight for him.

Fight to make him see. Fight to convince him that she'd made a mistake. That she wanted to try again.

But she was so tired of fighting.

Battling with a teenager was hard enough. She didn't want to go into another battle she wasn't sure she could win.

Besides, nothing had changed. She was still in a situation where she couldn't commit to him. Her life was on hold for the foreseeable future and he deserved more than crumbs.

Sure, Brent had always wanted a family—but wanting one from scratch, one that was all shiny and new, and inheriting one were two different things. The Brent she'd known had wanted a handful of kids and a house in the suburbs complete with the white picket fence.

He'd wanted perfection.

Would he want this family? This out-of-control, dysfunctional, grieving, far-from-perfect family?

Grace pulled her pillow over her head and rubbed her face into it hard.

Brent was right. This was crazy.

* * *

A miserable, sleepless week followed. Grace tried to avoid Brent at work but the harder she tried, the more she ran into him. He seemed to be around every corner. Smiling and chatty and being so damn nice to her, her whole body ached.

Her face ached from her fake smile, her head ached from being perennially pleasant and her heart ached from the constant cramp it seemed to contract into whenever he was near.

But she smiled and chatted back, acted like everything was fine, pretended her whole house-of-cards existence hadn't just had several cards removed. The ache that had dulled and which she'd trained herself to ignore over the years was back, and she was going to have to learn to live with it all over again.

Breaking it off twenty years ago had been one of the most difficult things she'd ever done. Deciding to stay away, deny her love, trumped that tenfold.

But it was the only way.

And in a strange sort of way she almost welcomed the pain. It was her punishment. For leaving him in the first place. Her comeuppance. Her due.

It was bitter, bitter irony.

It was exactly what she deserved.

By the time Sunday came around again she was a wreck. She'd barely slept, she had a giant headache and her hands trembled from the multiple cups of coffee she'd been existing on just to get through the week.

And to add to her woes she and Tash had a massive argument just before leaving for the oval for Benji's footy game. Her niece announced she was going to a friend's house for the day and wouldn't be attending the game.

Grace saw red.

She yelled. Actually yelled. She'd always been so calm and measured before, reining in her temper, preferring to use unruffled reasoning. To treat Tash like an adult. She'd never tried to be Julie, knowing instinctively that Tash would react very badly to any attempts to be mothered.

But this was the last straw.

Tash was grounded. And Grace discovered that calm and reasoned could last only so long in the continuing face of a badly behaved teenager hell-bent on self-destruction.

When they arrived at the oval an hour later Grace added a sore throat to her list of physical ailments. And one sulky, rebellious teenager.

Benji bounced over to his team the second he alighted the car and Grace watched with an aching heart as Brent squeezed her nephew's shoulder and grinned down at him.

Grace joined the huddle at a more sedate pace, needing time to suppress her body's reaction to Brent looking all big and broad and sexy as hell surrounded by a group of kids who plainly hero-worshipped him.

Surrounded by his urban family.

Brent smiled as she approached. 'Are you okay?' he asked. She looked tired. Sexy tired in jeans and a skivvy that hugged all the right places, but tired nonetheless.

Grace nodded and diverted her gaze from the concern in Brent's tawny eyes to Benji high-fiving his teammates. 'Fine,' she said. 'Just had a…difference of opinion with Tash.'

Brent glanced at the teenager, who hadn't moved from the car. Her deep scowl and furrowed brow were plainly visible even from this distance. It wasn't a face that would have launched a thousand ships.

'She doesn't look happy.' Neither did Grace.

Grace shrugged. 'Let's just say I'm not her favourite person this morning.'

The note of defeat in Grace's voice grabbed at his gut. He tossed the football from one hand to the other as he searched her face. It was free of make-up except for the usual coating of Honey Jumble lip gloss, the smell of which wafted towards him, trumping the aroma of cut grass.

The last week, no matter how many times he told himself it was crazy, the idea that they could start over had slipped beneath his defences.

He smiled at her. 'If it helps, you're one of my favourite people.'

Grace glanced at him, startled by words that sounded utterly sincere. She looked for a sign he was being disingenuous, maybe even joking, but his steady, smiling face was reassuring.

'Yes, actually,' she admitted with a half-smile. 'It probably seems a bit pathetic, but it does.'

Brent grinned, their gazes locking. 'Good.'

Suddenly she found herself grinning back, the weight on her shoulders easing as her heart bloomed beneath the warmth of his smile, her love growing bigger again.

And for a moment it felt like they were the only two people on earth.

'Come on, Brent,' Benji said, relieving Brent of the ball. 'Let's play.'

Brent dragged his gaze from Grace's and looked down at the kids. 'Okay, team. Line up over at the posts.' He winked at Grace. 'Catch you later.'

Grace nodded silently and finally remembered to breathe.

A few hours later they were nearing the end of the Perry family friendly when Grace noticed that Tash, who had refused to participate and had sat on the sideline, texting, for nearly an hour, was now notably absent.

Her heart began to beat a little harder as a prickle of dread mixed with the bead of cold sweat that was trekking slowly down her spine. She craned her neck, letting her gaze sweep the greater area of the park in ever-widening circles. Finally she spotted a few forms behind a clump of gum trees at the furthest reaches of the park.

She couldn't actually tell if one of them was Tash or even if there were three or four of them, but Grace knew in her bones that her niece was among their number.

'I'm out,' she called as she stalked off the field and headed towards the gum trees.

No amount of lecturing herself about staying calm helped the spike in her blood pressure when the distinct aroma of tobacco smoke assaulted her as she drew nearer.

In fact, Grace was pretty much near boiling point as she bore down on the oblivious teenagers. Three girls and a boy.

'Natasha!'

Four startled faces almost choked on their cigarettes as they whipped round to face her. Before her niece had a chance to do or say anything, Grace pulled the offending item from her lips, threw it to the ground and stomped on it hard.

The others all dropped their cigarettes too.

'Do your parents know you're down here, smoking behind their backs?' Grace demanded, looking hard at each teenager.

'Aunty Grace!'

Grace ignored the horrified plea from her niece. 'Go home,' she said, lowering her voice to a growl as she continued to eyeball them. 'Right now!'

'Aunty Grace!'

'Its okay, Tash,' the boy said, his eyes darting nervously between Tash and Grace. He gave her a quick hug, as did the girls, and they took off without a backward glance.

'That was so not cool,' Tash said, shaking her head at her aunt, her mouth a thin, bitter line.

Grace gave her an incredulous look. 'Do you think I give two hoots about being cool?'

'Obviously not,' Tash threw at her.

Grace ignored her and held out her palm to her niece. 'Give them to me,' she demanded. 'The cigarettes.'

Tash shook her head, mutiny in her eyes. 'I don't have any.'

Grace kept her hand out. 'I don't believe you.'

Tash gasped. 'You can't treat me like this.'

Grace kept her hand out but sucked in a breath, reaching for patience. 'If you're endangering your life, I can.' She waggled her fingers. 'If I have to wrestle you to the ground, I will.'

Tash shook her head as tears filled her eyes, looking at her aunt as if Grace had just grown a second head. 'I can't believe this,' she said, opening her bag, reaching in and pulling out the packet. She slapped it into Grace's palm.

Grace opened them and pulled one out. She ripped it in half and threw it in the dirt. 'Are you trying to kill yourself?' she demanded, as she pulled out another, tore it in half as well, throwing it down to join the other.

'Lung cancer.' She pulled out and tore one more. 'Emphysema.' Another one hit the ground. 'Heart disease. Nicotine addiction.'

By the time Grace got to the end of the long line of smoking-related medical conditions, every one had been broken and was lying in the dirt at their feet.

Tash was staring at her aunt, open-mouthed, shaking her head. 'Are you crazy?' she yelled.

'Crazy?' Grace yelled back, her head ready to explode right off her shoulders. 'I'm not the one who's smoking. Who's polluting pristine lungs.' She poked Tash in the chest. 'See this picture?'

Grace pointed to the graphic image of a cancerous lung that the government decreed all cigarette packets must display.

'Do you have some kind of death wish? Do you think your parents would approve of you smoking?'

Tash balled her hands into fists by her sides. 'You are such a…bitch!'

Grace gasped as if she'd been slapped. Had Tash really just called her *that* name? Had she heard right?

'What is the matter with you?' she demanded, grabbing Tash's upper arms and giving her a shake. 'Why are you acting like this?' This wasn't the Tash she'd known. 'This isn't you, Tash. I know things are hard for you at the moment but they will get better, I promise. This isn't the way to go about it.'

'Leave me alone,' Tash said, wrenching herself away. 'Just leave me alone.'

'No, Tash,' Grace said, shaking her head. 'No. You mightn't like me very much right now but I'm not ever leaving you alone. I love you.'

Brent could hear the raised voices from quite a way away and he quickened his pace. Grace's mother had asked him to go and investigate after the game had ended and he'd been happy to oblige.

But did he want to get into the middle of this? It was obviously personal and he wasn't sure it would be appreciated.

All of this week the insidious thought that maybe he and Grace could make another go of it had been insinuating itself into his grey matter. But this was the stark reality of Grace's life. She came with two orphaned kids—one of them a very angry teenager.

It was a reality check he wasn't sure he wanted when the fantasy was much prettier.

But then he saw Grace grab Tash and something deeper, something primitive overrode his hesitation and spurred him on.

'Everything all right here?' he asked moments later.

Grace and Tash, both obviously engrossed in their slanging match, looked at him like he'd just landed from Mars.

'Brent,' Grace said. He looked so good and capable and she just wanted to go to him and sob all over his shirt, absorb all that strength that seemed to ooze from his every pore.

Brent took one look at the scene—the smell of smoke, several shredded cigarettes in the dirt, a furious-looking Grace, a tearful Tash—and summed it up in a second.

He looked at Grace and then at Tash. 'Come with me,' he said.

CHAPTER TWELVE

TEN minutes later they were in his car and a tense silence had descended. Tash was in the back, staring stonily out the window. Grace, sitting in the front seat, her stomach churning and her brain tumbling, turned to face Brent.

'Brent?' she asked quietly.

He glanced at her briefly, before returning his eyes to the road. 'Trust me,' he murmured, reaching out and giving her knee a quick squeeze before returning it to the steering-wheel.

The action was so comforting that Grace almost covered his hand with hers but it was so brief his hand was gone before she had the chance.

She did trust him. *Implicitly.*

Ten more minutes and they were pulling into Brent's car parking space at the Central.

'What are we doing here?' Tash asked.

Brent ignored the huffy note in the teenager's voice. 'I have someone I want you to meet.'

Tash looked like she was about to object but Grace shot her a my-patience-is-running-out look and she climbed out of the car.

They walked through the emergency department, greeting staff as they went but not stopping as Brent ushered them into the lift and pushed the fifth-floor button. No one spoke for the brief ride and then they were out and Brent was shepherding them into ward 5C.

He walked down the hallway until he found room nine and strode in, with Grace and Tash following. A man was sitting hunched on the side of the bed, his legs dangling over the edge. He was grey and breathless, with plastic oxygen prongs in his nose.

'Hi, Bill,' he said.

Bill looked up and smiled. 'Hey…Doc,' he murmured, his pursed lips grabbing for air between the words.

Grace recognised the man instantly. William Loch. She'd admitted him a couple of days ago for exacerbation of his chronic obstructive airways disease.

'I've brought you someone to meet, Bill,' Brent said. 'You know Dr Perry, of course, and this is her niece Natasha.'

Bill nodded at Grace and smiled at Tash. 'And to what…do I…owe the…pleasure?' he puffed.

'Tash here has taken up smoking,' Brent said.

'Ah,' Bill said. And then laughed. It wasn't the first teen smoker that Brent had brought his way and he was more than happy to oblige with a little public health education—anything to get the message out to kids.

Bill's laugh stimulated a cough. And then another and then he couldn't stop. Great hacking coughs that tore at his throat. He held his chest and pointed at a Styrofoam cup on his bedside table, indicating for Tash to pass it to him.

She picked it up, looking down as she passed it on, recoiling from the yellowy-green slimy substance in the bottom flecked with blood. Tash dropped it quickly into Bill's hand and watched in horror as he coughed up another disgusting-looking globule of gross-coloured sputum.

'Thanks,' he said, when the coughing fit had passed.

'Mr Loch is a respiratory cripple,' Brent said to Tash. 'Thanks to smoking.'

Bill nodded. 'Started when I…was your age… Stupidest thing I…ever did.'

He looked down at his hands and held them up so Tash could see the unsightly orangey-yellow stains on his fingers. Tash took them in along with the shocking state of Bill's heavily yellow teeth.

'Take my advice, girlie…don't start… choose life… This is no…no kind of life.'

Bill tired quickly and they left the room a couple of minutes later with a rather subdued Tash. Neither of them said anything to her. They knew that the message had been well and truly taken on board.

They rode the lift back to the emergency department. Tash needed to use the toilet and Grace showed her to the staff facilities. 'We'll just be in there,' Grace said, pointing to the door of the staffroom just down from the loo.

She joined Brent in the deserted staffroom, the door swishing silently closed behind her. He was lounging against the sink, drinking a glass of water. 'Want one?' he asked.

She nodded. 'Thanks.'

Brent pulled a glass down from the cupboard above the sink and filled it at the bench-top bubbler. He passed it to her, settling back against the sink again, crossing one ankle over the other. He clinked his glass against hers. 'Here's to Bill.' He smiled.

Grace laughed. She felt like she hadn't been happy for a week and it was good to at last have a reason to laugh. 'That was ingenious, thank you.'

'Bill and I have an arrangement. Quite a few foster-kids have found themselves passing Bill's sputum cup.'

Grace laughed again, remembering Tash's look of disgust. 'I guess it's handy to have a respiratory cripple up your sleeve.'

Brent grinned and Grace felt her breath hitch as tall, dark and handsome morphed into sublimely sexy. She sipped at her water to hide the sudden rush of lust blooming from her core. Her gaze dropped and centred on his throat as he took another deep swallow of his water.

The bloom rippled ever outwards and her nipples tightened just thinking about laying her lips against the heavy pulse that thudded at the base of his throat. She remembered how good he smelled right there.

Brent swallowed, his throat suddenly parched. His gaze

locked on her mouth, watching as it pressed against the glass, her lips moist. They'd be cool against his throat, at the spot where she was staring. And wet. Maybe they'd even sizzle on contact.

He flicked his gaze upwards and their eyes met. Hers looked large behind the frames of her glasses. And hot. Like steaming thermal pools.

The heat radiated towards him and he felt a corresponding warmth seep into him. They were close, close enough for him to pull her towards him.

Maybe they *could* pick up where they'd left off?

'Maybe,' he said, reaching for her, their gazes still locked as his finger hooked through a loop on her waistband, 'this isn't so crazy.'

He tugged and pulled her slowly towards him. She didn't object.

Grace's heart gave a little leap as their bodies touched. He shifted, settling her against him as his breath fanned her cheek. She held his gaze, watched it shimmer with desire.

Brent lifted a lock of her fringe with a finger and tucked it behind her ear. 'I want to kiss you,' he murmured. 'Is that crazy?'

Grace heart pounded like a freight train in her chest, thrumming through her ears. His fingers stroked down her cheek and his thumb teased the corner of her mouth. She swallowed. 'Probably.'

Brent smiled. He held her gaze for a moment longer and then slowly inched his mouth towards hers.

Just as his lips brushed hers a loud knock followed by 'Aunty Grace?' burst into their sexual bubble, and they leapt apart like a couple of teenagers being sprung by their parents. Brent turned to face the sink, emptying his glass, and Grace took two paces away from him and faced the door.

'In here,' she called.

Tash opened the door. 'Can we go?' she asked. The

abruptness of her request was tempered by the contriteness of her tone.

Grace cleared her throat. 'Sure.' She glanced at Brent and then quickly away. 'Let's go,' she announced, making a hasty exit.

Brent followed Grace at a more sedate pace, still rattled, needing time to recover from their near kiss.

If only Tash had waited another minute...

But it was a good reminder that with two kids in the mix Grace's life was full of interruptions. It wasn't just her any more. And as much as he'd like to think they could recapture what they'd had, it plainly wasn't possible.

Things seemed to settle with Tash over the next couple of weeks, which freed Grace's head space up for other more pleasurable things—like daydreaming about the Brent possibilities.

His *maybe this isn't so crazy* fuelled an avalanche of fantasies and she let them have free rein.

Maybe he would fall in love with her again? Maybe they could be together.

Working with him became the highlight of her days. Even though they didn't touch and they didn't talk about Brent's *maybe this isn't so crazy*, there was a vibe between them now.

They stopped in the corridors to chat to each other. They ate lunch together. They joked. They reminisced about their uni days. His gaze would often drop to her mouth when she was talking or eating, and occasionally she'd be checking out his butt as he walked away and he'd turn and wink at her.

She felt all warm and delicious inside for the first time in a long time instead of edgy and anxious.

She sprang out of bed on work days and thoughts of him filled the non-work days. And the Sunday footy match was heavily anticipated by more than Benji.

It was a good opportunity to be near him and not have to be professional. Where they were just Brent and Grace. Not Dr

Cartwright and Dr Perry. To able to laugh and play and flirt and build on their relationship outside the confines of work.

Neither of them broached the subject of the future but, with two weeks of exemplary behaviour from Tash, so much seemed possible.

Until at two one morning her mobile rang and changed everything.

Grace sat bolt upright in bed, completely disorientated, groping for her phone, the light, her glasses as the ring pealed insistently. It was raining outside, drumming on the roof, a good foil to her drumming heart.

Grace was all fingers and thumbs at this hour, trying to find the damn thing quickly so as not to wake the kids. The lamplight blinded her as the possibilities stomped through her brain like stampeding elephants. A ringing phone at this time of night was never good news. She wasn't on call, so what was it?

Had something happened to her parents?

Please, dear God, no, she couldn't bear another loss.

At last, through a combination of cramming her glasses on her face and squinting, she located her phone and hit the answer button, her heart pounding.

'Hello?'

'Grace? It's Brent.'

It took a few seconds for Grace to recognise the voice on the other end was Brent's, even though her body recognised the deep rumble on a completely primal level.

'Grace?'

'Sorry—yes, I'm here.'

She snuggled down beneath the covers, her heart rate settling. She didn't know why he was ringing her at this hour of the morning but his voice sounded all sleepy and sexy and she wanted to curl up and listen to him as the rain kept up its steady beat on the roof.

Maybe he'd rung to talk about the thing growing between

them? Maybe he'd been lying awake night after night too, fantasising about them?

'I'd forgotten what a sexy voice you have,' she murmured, her inhibitions blunted by drowsiness, her eyes already shutting as she yawned.

'Grace, I need you to listen. Are you awake?'

'Mmm.' She sighed, snuggling further under the covers.

'Grace!'

Grace opened her eyes at his abrupt command. 'What?' she said crankily.

'I'm at work—'

That's right. He was on call. 'You want me to come in?'

He was ringing about a work matter? She sat up a little, the bubble created by the darkened room, the rain and his sexy voice well and truly bursting. 'I can't, Brent. The kids are asleep.'

'Grace, Tash is here. She's all right but she's been in an accident.'

Grace frowned and sat up even higher. She gave a half-laugh, 'What? No. She's in bed sound asleep.'

'Grace…'

Grace was silent for a moment then she was kicking aside the bed covers. 'She's in bed,' she insisted, padding through the house, picking up speed as she got closer to her niece's room.

Empty.

The bed was empty.

Grace pushed a hand into her hair, her heartbeat thundering in time with the rain again. But she'd checked on Tash before she'd gone to bed at ten. She'd kicked the covers off and Grace had pulled them back up.

'Oh, God. Is she injured?' Panic slammed into her. White hot, burning. Grace stalked to her bedroom, dragging on jeans. 'What? Tell me what?'

'She's fractured her ankle. It's a simple fracture and won't need surgical intervention. There's a lot of swelling so we've put it in a backslab for now and we'll admit her overnight for observation.'

'Oh, God,' Grace wailed. 'I don't believe this. How? She was asleep five hours ago!'

'They were all very lucky.'

'They!'

'Just get here Grace, okay? I can tell you the rest when you get here.'

Grace sucked in a breath. His voice was calm and she latched on to it. 'That's it, right? You're not trying to sugar-coat this? That's all?'

'Just some bumps and bruises…that's all. No other…physical injuries.'

'Right,' Grace said, her mind racing ahead in time with the gallop of her heartbeat, deaf to the hesitation in Brent's voice. 'I'll be there in…' Hell! How long would it take to get her mum here? She couldn't think. 'I don't know, half an hour.'

'Drive carefully, Grace, please. There's no point having you both in hospital.'

Grace made it in forty-three minutes. She screeched to a halt in the ambulance bay, uncaring that it was for emergency vehicles only. Brent greeted her at the sliding doors.

'Where is she?' Grace demanded.

He placed a restraining hand on her arm as she stormed inside. She was wearing jeans and a V-necked skivvy with a hoodie and, even frantic, with no make-up on except her regulation lip gloss and a blanket mark still visible on her face, she looked beautiful.

'Just wait for a moment,' he said. 'I need to talk to you.'

'Oh, God—what?' Grace clutched her stomach, grabbed his arm. 'What's happened?'

Brent slid his palms up her arms and gently grasped her upper arms. 'Nothing's happened. She's exactly the same as I told you on the phone. But there's something you need to know before you go charging in there.'

Grace looked at him sharply. There was something he wasn't telling her, she could hear it in his voice. She was torn between demanding to know and burying her head in his chest and bawling her eyes out.

Brent could see he had Grace's full attention now and he took a breath before imparting what he was fairly certain was going to be very unwelcome news. He wished he could shelter her from it but it had to be said.

'She's drunk, Grace. Her blood-alcohol level has come back at double the legal limit.'

Grace felt an instant denial rise to her lips. 'It must be wrong.'

Brent shook his head. 'She's pretty wasted.'

Grace stared at him in disbelief. Was this truly happening? But looking into Brent's steady tawny gaze, she knew this was very, very real.

A surge of anger joined the volatile mix of fear and anxiety that had been rampaging through her system. Apart from a couple of notable incidents, she'd been pussy-footing around Tash for ages now, trying to give her space and show her faith and trust, and this was what she got?

First smoking and now sneaking out and drinking and getting into car accidents?

Grace looked at Brent in utter dismay, finally truly broken. Was this what happened when she took her eye off the ball? When she dared to start thinking about herself?

'Tell me all of it.'

Tash was asleep when Grace flicked back the curtain and she felt all the anger and frustration melt away at how small and fragile Tash looked on the gurney. She looked twelve, not fifteen.

So young and innocent.

Tash's eyes fluttered open, taking in the two grim-faced adults looking down at her. Her lips twisted. 'I told you not to call her,' she said, ignoring Grace and glaring at Brent. Belligerence dripped from her slurred voice.

'Tash!'

'Oh, what?' the teenager demanded. Her mascara had run and big round panda eyes stabbed hostility towards her. 'What do you care anyway?'

Grace felt as if Tash had slugged her with a knuckleduster. She sucked in a breath, fighting to stay calm.

It didn't work.

'What do you mean?' she asked, crossing to stand beside the gurney. 'Of course I care, you stupid girl,' she yelled. 'You think it doesn't worry me sick that you're sneaking out in the middle of the night, getting drunk, getting in cars with drunk people, running into power poles?'

Grace could feel her fingers trembling and she wrapped them around the gurney's metal safety rails. 'You could have been killed,' she snarled. 'You all could have been killed.'

'Yeah, well—at leasht I'd be wiv Mum.'

Grace felt cold fingers clutch her heart. Did Tash have some kind of death wish? She'd asked her that a couple of weeks ago during the cigarette incident but what if her niece really was suicidal?

'Do you think that your mother would want you dead at fifteen? Do you?' Grace demanded, her voice getting higher. She could feel her tightly wound control unravelling. 'Because I can tell you for absolutely bloody certain that she wouldn't. She'd be horrified.'

Tash reared up. 'Don't you talk to me about my mother,' she shouted. 'How would you know? You were never here.'

Grace blinked as alcohol fumes and spittle from her niece's impassioned tirade sprayed her face. More black tears flowed down Tash's face and Grace felt her own building.

'Where were you when she needed you the mosht? You the great docter! You could have saved her.' Tash stabbed her finger at Grace's shoulder. 'But you were too bishy wiv your great important life. You didn' love her. She needed you and you let her die.'

'Natasha! That will do!' Brent's voice sliced through the teenager's hysteria as he stepped forward and placed his hand on Grace's shoulder. 'Your aunt is not to blame for your mother's death.'

Tash burst into tears and turned on her side away from them both, loud sobs echoing around the cubicle.

Grace sucked in a breath, disbelief pounding through her skull. She was pleased for Brent's solid presence behind her as her entire world tilted around her. Hot tears welled in her eyes and slipped down her cheeks.

She'd known Tash was angry, but not over this. Tash blamed her for not being around? For not being at the Royal Melbourne Hospital that night, working, when her sister had needed an emergency physician?

How could her niece know that she blamed herself for the same thing? That the guilt about being so far away from Julie, from her family, when it had happened had been so profound it still lingered to this day?

She looked at Tash's back, watching the heaving of her shoulders, desperately wanting to reach out and touch her despite still reeling from her vitriol.

But knowing Tash would never accept it. Not at the moment.

The gap between them had never felt wider.

Brent felt Grace sag back against him and he gently stroked his thumb up and down the vertebral ridges at the back of her neck. He'd watched with dismay as Tash's barbs had hit Grace square in the chest.

The two Perry women were hurting—their pain was like a force-field in the cubicle, arcing between them, pushing each other apart like two opposing magnetic fields.

He wished he could take away their pain.

Gabi stuck her head behind the curtain, looking uncertainly at Brent and Grace. 'The ward's ready for Natasha now.'

'Thanks, Gabs. Let's get her transferred.'

Twenty minutes later Tash was ensconced in the orthopaedic ward, her lower leg in a half-plaster at the back to support the fracture but allowing for more swelling. It was elevated on two pillows.

She complained of pain and a nurse administered some intravenous pain relief.

Grace wasn't surprised. She felt ill, looking at the blue and purple joint, which was puffed up to the point of being unrecognisable as an ankle. What if it had been her head?

She shuddered at the hundreds of horrifying possibilities—the things that could have happened.

In fact, Tash, sitting in the front passenger's seat, which had been the point of impact, had come off worst. The driver and other passenger, girls from Tash's school, had suffered only minor injuries. Seat-belt bruising—which luckily hadn't damaged the spleen—and a head laceration from hitting the steering-wheel.

Tash and Grace hadn't spoken in anything more than a perfunctory manner since their earlier argument, and when the nurse left the room there was just the two of them and the things that had been said lying large and loud between them.

Tash settled herself against the pillows. 'You should go home,' she said to the ceiling. 'I'll be fine.'

Grace didn't take her eyes off her niece. 'I'm staying.'

Tash rolled away—as much as she could with her injured leg elevated—and Grace was left to stare at the back of Tash's head.

And worry.

CHAPTER THIRTEEN

AN HOUR later, Grace stood. She couldn't sit a minute longer in the uncomfortable plastic chair, listening to the continual treadmill of her thoughts. Tash's anger had been shocking. Even more so on continuous loop through her head. It was terrible to realise that her niece had been harbouring such thoughts for the last eighteen-plus months.

You let her die.

No wonder Tash had been treating her so disparagingly.

Grace paced around the small single room for a while, staring out the window at the wet streets of the car park and beyond, the reflections of traffic lights in the puddles making the streets look all shiny and new.

A great night to be tucked up in bed.

She looked over her shoulder at Tash. She was sleeping soundly, her panda eyes making her look even more disconsolate. There were times she looked so much like Julie it was spooky.

Grace was reminded again of the incident when she and Brent had had to rescue Julie from imminent alcohol poisoning. Her sister had looked just as wretched that night. And if memory served her correctly, she'd felt even more wretched the next day.

Tash was going to have one hell of a headache in the morning.

Grace turned back to the window, her gaze falling on Brent's sporty little convertible in the car park. The one they'd made out in like they had both still been eighteen.

Before he'd told her they couldn't pick up where they'd left off.

Before she'd realised she still loved him.

Before his *maybe this isn't so crazy.*

Before he'd had to ring her and tell her that her inebriated niece had been in a car crash.

She pressed her forehead against the window pane, the moist coolness like soothing balm. She recalled his hand on her shoulder, the stroke of his thumb at her nape. Giving her an anchor, something to lean on. Thank God it had been him on duty tonight. Someone who knew. Who cared.

It seemed like he was always there for the Perry women and their alcohol-related crises.

She'd give anything now to be held by him. To bury her face in his shirt and have him tell her it was all going to be all right. That he loved her. That he'd be by her side.

But if tonight had demonstrated anything to her, it had demonstrated that Grace had failed in her responsibility as Tash's guardian. That while she'd been building an imaginary castle in the air, Tash had still been feeling wretched enough to sneak out of the house and put her life in danger.

How had she missed that?

She wouldn't let her attention be hijacked again.

So she couldn't go to him for comfort. But she could go and thank him for tonight. For not listening to Tash and ringing her. For coming to her defence during Tash's drunken tongue-lashing.

She turned. Tash was fast asleep and between the medication and alcohol probably would be for hours. Her gaze wandered to the uninviting contours of the hard plastic chair.

Stretching her legs seemed a much better option.

Brent had just laid his head on the couch when the knock sounded on the door. He sighed. So much for sleep. He threw the blanket off, rose and padded across to the door, unlocking it and pulling it open.

'Oh,' he said as he took in Grace, her hands shoved in the front pockets of her jeans, an uncertain look on her face.

He'd fought the urge to go and visit her up on the ward before crashing in the on-call room. Grace had seemed so defeated by Tash's accusations, so…lost that he hadn't been sure he wanted to put himself in the midst of that.

Visions of that night in the tree house and in his car had been powerful reminders that a vulnerable Grace quickly slipped under his skin. Neutralising his resistance.

And the last thing she needed now was him complicating things further.

He'd planned instead to go visiting in the morning before he went home. With some sleep under his belt. And a modicum of perspective.

'Hi.'

'Hi,' he said. 'Is everything okay…with Tash?'

'Oh, yes.' Grace nodded vigorously. 'She's sleeping soundly. I just…'

She just what? Brent was standing at the door, looking all solid and warm, and she'd been fooling herself that coming to see him had been about gratitude. He looked weary and wary; his hand high up on the doorframe was not an inviting gesture. It quite clearly said, *Do not enter.*

Obviously this incident with Tash had been a wake-up call for him. He had probably suddenly realised what he was getting himself into with his flirty eyes and sexy laughter these last couple of weeks.

Tears pricked at her eyes as the enormity of this lost opportunity to love him slammed into her.

'I'm sorry…' Her voice was husky as a lump of emotion welled in her throat. She sucked in a ragged breath as she blinked back tears. 'You're trying to sleep. It doesn't matter.'

Brent sighed. Keeping his arm up high, he pulled the door open a little further. 'Come in.'

Grace knew it was her chance to be strong. To tell him to go to bed, that she'd see him later. But she was tired of being strong. She wanted to suck up some of that Brent confidence, if only for a little while.

She'd just stay for a little while.

She ducked in under his arm, his familiar scent embracing her, confirming the rightness of it all.

Brent shut the door quietly, pressing his forehead against the wood briefly, taking a moment to breathe as he flipped the lock. He turned and walked towards her, his heart rate picking up, his senses on high alert.

Grace fought to bring her overwhelming emotions under control, twisting her hands. Fingers of light from the outside corridor filtered through the blinds, illuminating the edges of the otherwise darkened room.

She stood in the middle, searching for the right words.

Words that did not start with L.

'I wanted to th-thank you,' she said. 'For everything tonight. I'm so glad it was you who was on. This whole thing with Tash...'

Grace stopped as a king tide of grief surged over her. She couldn't go on. She ducked her head as her eyes misted and a tear spilled down her cheek.

Brent's first instinct was to reach for her. He resisted. It was just too dangerous. He wanted her too much. But standing here, watching her cry, he felt so helpless. He hated seeing her cry. Always had.

His blood beat through his veins, thick and sludgy, thrumming through his head to a primal rhythm.

Grace looked up at him. 'She hates me.'

Brent sucked in a breath at the anguish in those three simple words. In her gaze.

Oh, hell.

He couldn't bear it. Watching her like this was too hard. And suddenly he knew why.

He was still in love with her.

The admission opened the floodgates and the emotions he'd held in check since she'd been back, the ones he'd buried all those years ago, rushed out at him, filling every cell and sinew of his body. They washed through his chest and flowed through his heart. They couldn't be denied any longer.

He loved her.

It wasn't a time for joy. If anything it was a complication so unbearable that for a moment he wanted to run far, far away. As far from her as he could. Thinking and wondering and fantasising about *being* with her again was a totally different prospect to *loving* her again.

Yet again, he loved this woman. And yet again, the gap yawned between them.

She was looking at him, waiting, with tears running down her cheeks. And he had nothing. Except the overwhelming imperative to keep her at arm's length lest he succumb to the potent dictates of his love.

But she was crying.

So he reached for her hand and tugged her towards him. She needed comfort. He couldn't deny the woman he loved that most basic human need.

It was just a hug.

'No, she doesn't.' He shut his eyes as she settled against him, honey and vanilla wrapping him in a hundred dangerous memories. 'She's drunk and I suspect angry with herself over her stupidity. She's just lashing out.'

Grace dropped her forehead onto his chest and leant into him, more hot tears falling. 'Yeah, but she's right, isn't she? If I'd been there…'

Brent looked down at her. He could see the doubt and the guilt and he couldn't bear the thought of her blaming herself for her sister's death. She'd been two thousand kilometres away, for crying out loud.

He slid his hand to her jaw and cradled her face. 'I've seen her file, Grace.' Brent had called in a favour at the Royal and read Julie's chart. 'Her injuries were fatal. No one could have saved her.'

'But—'

'Shh.' Before he knew what he was doing he dropped a kiss on her forehead. It came so easy. Felt so natural.

Grace blinked up at him. 'I miss her,' she whispered.

Brent heard a whole spectrum of emotions in those three simple words. Pain, sadness, regret, longing. More hot tears welled in her eyes and he felt his resistance melt as each one fell.

His pulse boomed in his ears, thundered in his chest as he came to a decision.

'I know,' he murmured, pulling off her glasses and kissing her tears away.

Between the tears, the dark and losing her glasses, the world went very blurry. 'Brent I…I can't see,' she protested half-heartedly, as his lips brushed her cheeks with infinite softness.

'Shh,' he murmured, dropping a kiss on the side of her mouth. 'Shut your eyes, you don't need them.'

Grace sighed, her eyes fluttering closed as surrender stole through her body. She whimpered as his breath fanned her lips. She bunched her fingers into his shirt as her legs threatened to give way. His arm slipped around her back, anchoring her to him.

His lips were tender when they brushed against hers. Gentle, like rain. And she soaked them up like parched earth, content for a while with light and tender. But then his tongue stroked along the soft pillow of her bottom lip and the slow fizz in her blood turned to a sizzle, burning bright and hot, and she opened her mouth wide and demanded he follow.

Brent groaned as the taste of honey taunted his taste buds and a surge of pure undiluted lust roared through his body. There was no thought of resistance now. This was Grace and he loved her and he might never be able to say the words but he could show her.

He could love her with his body tonight.

Cherish her.

Show her she was his everything.

His tongue plundered her mouth, his hand in her hair holding her head fast. His thumb tilted her chin back more, angling her head further, letting him go deeper, harder, with the kiss. She moaned against his mouth and he went deeper still.

He dropped his hand to her neck, stroking his fingers down her throat, rubbing his thumb over the frantic beat at the base. He dragged his mouth from hers, following the path of his fingers—across her jaw, down her throat, along her collar bone.

He felt her hands beneath his shirt, exploring the planes of his back, pushing beneath the waistband of his jeans, grasping his buttocks. He shut his eyes momentarily as his erection twitched, straining against the confines of cotton and denim.

Then he was nuzzling her cleavage, swiping his tongue across the rise of her breast. He held her close, his hand splayed between her shoulder blades as he dragged aside her shirt, her bra, his mouth seeking her nipple, finding it. She gasped and arched her back as he sucked it into his mouth, laved it, felt it grow taut and puckered against his tongue.

Grace almost fainted from the exquisite torture his mouth was dishing out. 'Brent,' she murmured, holding his head fast to her breast with one hand, fumbling with his fly with the other. Needing to touch him again. Wanting to grasp all that hardness. Desperate to feel it inside her again.

It had been too long. Twenty years without this. Without Brent. Without touching him, kissing him. Needing him.

Finally her hand lowered his zipper, his undies and she was freeing him, touching him—big and hard and hers.

Even if it was just for now.

Brent groaned against her breast as she swiped her thumb across the swollen tip of him. He lifted his head, sought her mouth again, sucked her lips against his, pushed his tongue inside her.

His eyes rolled back as she ran her hands up and down his shaft and he broke the kiss off. He grabbed at his shirt, pulling it over his head. 'Naked,' he gasped. 'Now.'

He grabbed her shirt, yanking it upwards, kissing her hard

on the mouth once it cleared her face. His fingers found her bra clasp and made short work of it. He stared at her for a moment, his breath heaving in and out, distracted by the beauty of her bare breasts.

But then she was unzipping her jeans and wiggling out of them and he did likewise and then they were totally naked together for the first time in twenty years and then somehow they were on the couch, Grace propped against the cushioned leather arm, her legs locked around his waist as he kissed down her neck, to her breasts and lower.

'Brent, no,' she panted as his overnight growth scratched her belly and muscles deep inside tightened to an unbearable ache. She pulled at his shoulders. 'I need to feel you inside me. Now.'

She wanted to be consumed by him. Branded. Connected to him in the most intimate way two humans could be. She didn't want foreplay.

She wanted possession.

Brent felt her hips move restlessly against his and saw fever in her gaze. Felt the answering call in his blood. His gut. His loins.

He was powerless to resist it.

He reached for the chair arm and dragged himself back to her as her legs locked him in place again. Then he was positioning himself, one forearm resting on the arm next to her head, the other grasping her hip, his engorged head nudging her hot slickness.

And with one push he was buried to the hilt and she was crying out, her head flung back, her mouth open, and he covered her mouth with his as he reared up over her with each thrust.

They set a rhythm that was uniquely theirs. Building and building with each thrust, each kiss, each groan. Deeper and deeper. Higher and higher. Their bodies telling each other things their mouths could not.

Reaching for the stars. Burning for each other brighter than any sun.

Grace dug her nails into his back as her climax built, rippling, undulating, twisting through her belly. She moaned against Brent's mouth.

'Yes,' he whispered. 'Yes.'

Grace whimpered. She clutched his shoulders, feeling them tremble, knowing he was near too, knowing he was as out of control as she was.

But for once she didn't care. She loved him. She was making love with him and it was the sweetest thing she'd known in for ever.

And then it broke over her and she screamed into his mouth as she clutched at his backside, holding him closer, deeper as she bucked and surged against him.

Brent felt her clamp hard around him and the slow, inexorable march to pleasure accelerated to warp speed and he was moaning into her mouth, bucking and grinding, thrusting wildly, pounding and thrashing and hammering. Pistoning in and out as he spilled into her high and hard, over and over, coming and coming and coming until he collapsed against her chest totally spent. Utterly exhausted.

They lay together for a while still joined, not moving, not speaking. Brent's weight pressed her into the lounge and she stroked his hair, his forehead, as their heart rates settled, their breathing slowed.

'I have to go back to Tash,' Grace said into the silence.

'I know.'

Another minute passed. A hundred other things she wanted to say tripped through Grace's head. But she didn't say any of them. She shifted and he moved off her. They dressed without looking at each other without saying a word, both too wary to speak at all in case the truth came out.

Grace slid her feet into her shoes and glanced at him. He was sitting on the lounge fully dressed, looking tired and handsome and very, very male. 'Thank you,' she said.

Brent gave a half-smile. 'My pleasure.'

Grace returned his half-smile with one of her own. 'I have to go.'

Brent nodded. 'I'll pop in and see Tash before I go home.'

Grace nodded back. Then she turned away and left the room.

Grace had a lot of time to think about the potential conse-quences of what had just transpired in the on-call room between her and Brent as she sat by Tash's bedside and dawn broke over Melbourne. But she didn't.

The implications needed a sharper brain to analyse them than the current state of her own, so there seemed little point. And she had no doubt that she'd think and rethink it *ad nau-seam* in the days and weeks to follow.

For now, she refused to sully its perfection, refused to feel guilt. For now she was happy just to relive it. The magic of his kiss. His touch. The way he still filled her so perfectly. The way only he knew how to bring her to the heights of dizziness through penetration alone. How he seemed to know exactly what she needed at exactly the right moment.

It was probably going to be her only chance to love him so completely. And if that was selfish then she refused to feel guilty about that too.

Tash shifted and frowned in her sleep and a little of that guilt raised its ugly head. Tash was what she should be think-ing about. Maybe if she'd been thinking more about Tash and less about Brent they wouldn't be in this predicament now.

But it was much easier to relive those thirty minutes with Brent than face the conundrum that was Tash.

Grace yawned as tiredness swamped her body. It had been a momentous night. Both physically and emotionally. An abrupt awakening combined with fear, stress, tears and a mind-blowing orgasm had taken its toll.

Suddenly, she was so, so tired.

She laid her head on Tash's bed, sliding her hand up the crisp white sheet to cover Tash's hand. Grace waited for her niece to move it away but when she didn't Grace relaxed and her eyes fluttered closed.

She'd just rest her eyes.

Just for a moment or two.

CHAPTER FOURTEEN

THE sun was streaming through the window when Grace woke to a noise a couple of hours later. She sat up abruptly, her neck and shoulders instantly protesting, her fingers numb and tingly from sleeping on her hand.

The noise came again and she turned quickly to face it. Tash was holding her head and groaning.

Grace stood and moved closer to her niece. 'Head bad?'

Tash nodded, cracking open an eyelid to look at Grace. 'I feel like someone's put my brain on the rack. It hurts worse than my ankle.'

Grace was tempted to give her a lecture about the perils of alcohol and let her suffer for a bit. But she'd never been the tough love kind of aunt and she knew she couldn't start now.

'I'll get some Panadol from the nurses. In the meantime,' she said, pouring a glass of water from the pitcher on the bedside table, 'drink this.'

Grace returned ten minutes later with two pills in her hand. She shook Tash's shoulder and Tash woke and downed the pills with another glass of water. Grace poured a third and insisted that Tash drink it.

'Alcohol dehydrates you. That's how come you have a headache,' she said, keeping it factual and non-judgmental. 'Rehydrate yourself and it'll help with the headache.'

Tash gulped it down without argument then sagged back against the pillows. 'Thanks,' she muttered.

Grace raised an eyebrow. *Progress.* 'How's the ankle?'

Tash looked down at her elevated limb. 'It's sore. But bearable.'

Grace nodded. She lifted her hand and felt lightly for the pedal pulse on top of Tash's foot. It had been marked with an X by the nurses for ease of finding it as they'd monitored it throughout the night.

Grace located the strong beat easily. It was good to feel the foot was warm, and when she lightly pressed on the skin the capillary refill was brisk. 'Can you wriggle your toes?' Tash wriggled. 'Any numbness?'

Tash shook her head. 'No.'

Grace sat down, satisfied. Her niece was lucky the swelling hadn't caused nervous or vascular compromise to her foot. They'd get another X-ray in a few days once the swelling had started to subside then a full cast would be applied.

Grace and Tash sat in silence for a few minutes. Grace came up with and discarded a variety of ways to talk about the previous night. Tash's eyes were closed but they did need to talk. Better here, while it was all still fresh, than at home in front of Benji.

'I'm sorry.'

Grace was startled out of her mental gymnastics by Tash's almost whisper. She looked at her niece. Her eyes were still closed. Had she imagined it?

Tash opened her eyes and looked at Grace. 'About the things I said last night. I'm sorry.'

Grace was stunned. She hadn't expected an apology. She'd expected excuses and more belligerence. More finger-pointing.

This was most definitely progress.

'Thank you,' Grace said. 'I appreciate that.'

She debated leaving it at that for now. Waiting for Tash to talk to her about things. But it wasn't a strategy that had worked thus far and her niece had given her an opening. Grace knew it would be foolish not to take it.

She drew her chair closer to the head of the bed. 'It's obviously how you've been feeling, though,' she said tentatively.

Tash opened her mouth to deny it but Grace waved her quiet. 'There's nothing quite like drunk honesty.'

Tash dropped her gaze to the bed covers. She sucked in a shaky breath. 'It makes it easier to have someone to blame.'

Grace nodded. 'Of course it does. I just wish I'd known earlier it was me you blamed. We could have talked about this instead of you bottling it up.'

Tash sniffed. 'I don't really, you know. Not deep down. I know rationally that you couldn't have saved her, that you lived thousands of kilometres away...'

Grace watched a tear trek down her niece's face as she struggled with her emotions, struggled to find the words. She covered Tash's hand with her own and gave it a squeeze. It felt incredibly good to have Tash squeeze back.

'I'm just so...so bloody...angry.' Tash balled her other hand into a fist and thumped it against the mattress. 'It's just not fair.'

Her voice cracked and she scrubbed at her face as more tears fell. 'And I do this thing with God, or whoever it is out there who's supposed to be in charge and doing a really, really lousy job...'

A sob tore from Tash's throat and she stuffed her hand against her mouth to stop any more coming out.

'Every night in bed I ask, beg, to be able to turn back time and have them safe at home with us that night and then, if I can't have that, I ask for you to be here in Melbourne and working at the hospital when she comes in and you save her.'

Grace swallowed against the lump in her throat, feeling useless and inadequate in the face of Tash's overwhelming grief.

'And every morning I wake up and they're still g-g-gone.' Her face crumpled and great heaving sobs tore from her mouth.

'Oh, Tash.' Grace pushed back the chair and threw herself on the edge of the mattress, dragging her niece towards her, hugging her close. 'Baby, I'm so sorry,' she whispered, rocking Tash back and forth.

'Why,' she sobbed into Grace's shoulder, 'do I keep thinking that tomorrow it will be d-different?'

Grace felt her own emotions spill over and she choked back her own tears—she wouldn't be any good to Tash if she also broke down. She eased back to look at Tash, wiping at her dirty mascara tears, pushing her fringe back from her face.

'You're grieving, darling. You're bargaining. It's normal and its natural and it's not anything I haven't done a thousand times also. Do you know how much I wish I'd been at the hospital that night? Do you know how many times I've asked to get those couple of hours back so I can change things?'

Tash shook her head vigorously at the doubt and agony on her aunt's face. 'No. No, please, I was wrong to say that. To think that. You loved Mum, she loved you. I'm so sorry, I didn't mean it. She missed you so much but she was so p-proud of you.'

Grace started to cry then. It was impossible not to. She pulled Tash back onto her shoulder and for the next few minutes the room was filled with the gut-wrenching sounds of two people grieving the loss of someone dear to them.

Someone they could never get back.

Tash eased away after a while and Grace looked at her. 'Better now?'

Tash nodded. 'Much.'

Grace squeezed her hand and sat back down in the chair.

Tash sagged against her pillows and shut her eyes for a moment. She opened them again and looked at Grace. 'Would you have come back sooner? If you'd known she was going to die?'

Grace didn't hesitate. 'Yes. Yes, yes, yes. A thousand times yes. I will always regret staying away for so long.'

She'd missed out on so much time with her sister. So much precious time. Her mind strayed to Brent. Maybe if she hadn't spent so much time away they'd be together again now.

Tash grimaced as she attempted to reposition her ankle and

Grace helped adjust the pillows. 'You girls were so lucky,' she murmured as the ugly bruising made her want to shudder.

Tash gave her aunt a guilty look. 'I'm so sorry. I deserve to be kicked out for what happened last night.'

'Oh, Tash, I'm not going to kick you out,' Grace chided. 'But I want you to talk to me. I want to know what's going on with you. What on earth possessed you to sneak out of the house last night? To get drunk? To get in a car with a drunk driver? It could have ended so much worse than it did.'

Tash shook her head. 'Since Mum and Dad died…I've just felt so…straitjacketed. I mean, life's short, right?' She turned pleading eyes on Grace. 'Any one of us could be dead tomorrow. I…we…know that better than anybody. I want to live, to experience it. To say yes to adventures.'

Grace's heart broke for Tash. She was still hurting so much. 'Smoking, getting drunk…they're no adventure, Tash. I'm sure your head will agree.'

Tash grimaced. 'Oh, yeah!'

'Sweetie…there's adventure and there's just plain old unsafe.'

'I don't want to play it safe, Aunty Grace. You didn't.'

'Oh, darling, I followed my dreams, yes, but they were hardly daredevil. There's a big difference between playing it safe and outright risky.'

Tash's chin wobbled. 'I know. I know.' She sniffed again. 'But you know what? Mum played it safe all her life. They always talked about seeing the world one day when they retired. I think she envied you, you know. I think…sometimes…she regretted having kids so young.'

Grace stilled as the note of uncertainty in her niece's voice clanged a loud bell.

'Hang on a moment, sweetheart.' She leaned forward in the chair. 'We might not have lived in each other's pockets for the last twenty years but I do know this—your mum only ever wanted a family. A husband and kids. The minute she met Doug that's all she talked about. All they talked about. And the second she found out she was pregnant with you she was utterly besotted.'

Grace paused to check that it was sinking in. 'She might have talked about travelling one day, might have had the odd moment of the grass being greener, but you can be absolutely certain that she died with no regrets about what she'd done with her life because you and Benji and your dad were all she ever wanted.'

Tash's face crumpled again. 'I don't want to die with regrets either, Aunty Grace.'

Grace stood and sat on the side of the bed again, grasping both her niece's forearms. 'And you won't. You're going to grow up and have great adventures, *safe adventures*, and grow old enough to tell your grandchildren all about them.'

Grace leaned forward and swept Tash's fringe off her face, 'Sweetie, you can't live your life thinking every day could be your last. I know that's what those bumper stickers say but it'll drive you crazy, Tash. And I'm pretty damn sure Julie wouldn't want you to live like that.'

Tash gave a wobbly smile. 'Mum would have killed me over last night.'

Grace laughed. 'Well, if it's any consolation, killing you did cross my mind last night too.'

Tash gave a half-laugh then blew out hard a few times, raising and lowering her shoulders, trying to stem another batch of tears. 'I'll be better from now on, I promise.'

Grace smiled, hooking Tash's fringe behind her ear, wiping at her wet cheeks. For the first time in eighteen months she actually felt like it was going to be okay. It had been an emotional eight hours. Cathartic. And she finally felt like Tash had bared her soul. Maybe now she could move forward. They all could.

Oh, Grace wasn't foolish enough to believe that Tash would be all sweetness and light from now on. She was, after all, still a teenager. There'd be battles won and lost. But she'd had a big scare and had finally unburdened herself.

It was a good start.

Grace kissed Tash's cheek. 'Good.'

Tash smiled and then grimaced. 'Ouch.'

'Ankle sore?'

Tash nodded. 'Very.'

Grace rang the call bell and within ten minutes the nurses had administered strong oral pain relief.

'Nod off for a while, Tash,' Grace said, straightening the sheet around her niece, fussing with the covers. 'I'll wait until you fall asleep and then I'll go home and pick up some toiletries and a change of clothes.'

Tash nodded, already closing her eyes. She made a grab for Grace's fingers and Grace was reminded of all the times as a child Tash had greedily monopolised her hand.

But it had never felt as sweet as it did right now.

'Tell me a memory,' she whispered.

Grace glanced at her niece's sleepy face, her heart thudding painfully in her chest, her throat tight with emotion. Grace swallowed the lump and opened her mouth.

'I remember one time when your mum was five and she wanted a skateboard…'

Ten minutes later Tash's fingers had slackened and her breathing was deep and even. Grace sat for another ten minutes just watching her niece sleep. She felt as if an enormous weight had been lifted from her shoulders and that she finally had Tash back.

Conscious of time slipping by, Grace eased her hand away. She had to go home and pick up some of Tash's things. She rose from the chair just as Brent strode into the room.

There was a moment of silence as they looked at each other. The memory of the on-call room stirred the air between them.

'Hi,' Grace said, her voice husky.

'Hi,' he replied standing in the doorway, hands on hips, before striding into the room. 'I came to see—'

'Shh.' Grace cut him off. She put a finger to her mouth and indicated a sleeping Tash. 'She's just had some pain relief.'

'Oh, sorry,' he said, treading quietly as he came closer to the foot of the bed. 'How's the ankle?' he whispered as he felt for her pedal pulse, his fingers a mere flutter against the bounding vessel.

'Sore.'

He nodded. 'And the head?'

Grace smiled despite her internal tumult. 'I think it's on level pegging with the ankle.'

Brent flicked a glance at her from the end of the bed. 'Are you—?'

'Shh,' Grace chided as Tash stirred. Brent's voice seemed to boom around the room.

Or was that just her crazy heart?

She grabbed his arm and ushered him over to the far corner.

'Sorry,' he apologised.

Grace shrugged. 'Its fine. Let's just keep it low, okay?' His scent surrounded her as he crowded close. She could smell herself on his skin, just as she could smell him on her.

'You look like you've been crying,' he murmured, suppressing the urge to sweep a lock of her fringe back behind her ear. He'd noticed the puffy redness behind her glasses the second he'd laid eyes on her face.

'Oh, yes,' Grace said, touching her face, embarrassed suddenly over her appearance. In eight hours she'd yelled, cried, been scared half to death, thoroughly loved and fallen asleep on a hard, small, plastic chair.

She must look a complete wreck.

Distracted by his cross-armed stance, which emphasised the broadness of his shoulders and chest, Grace looked at her feet.

'Tash and I have been doing a lot of talking. And crying.' Grace gave a quiet half-laugh and then looked at him. 'I think she's going to be okay, Brent.'

She wanted him to know that. Needed him to know. Not that it would make a difference but she knew that he cared about her niece as well.

'I know there's still a long row to hoe. It's not going to be all plain sailing, but we made a real breakthrough.'

Brent could feel her relief, her hope, deep in his soul. He wanted to put his arms around her, place his hands on her shoulders and pull her close. But just because things were changing for Grace on the home front, it didn't mean anything had changed with them.

She'd just said there was still a long row to hoe. And he wasn't going to put his heart on the line again. He could live with unrequited love—he'd done it for ages after she'd left twenty years ago.

He couldn't live with her rejecting him one more time. Even if he understood her motivation.

'That's great,' he said, stuffing his hands into his pockets, keeping his voice low. 'Really great, Grace.'

Grace heard his genuine happiness and beamed at him. 'It's such a relief.'

He smiled. Joy shone in her eyes, sparkling like diamonds in mist from her grey eyes. 'I bet.'

They fell silent then, still looking at each other, their smiles slowly dying as the memories of their passionate encounter reared between them again and the smell of sex heated the air.

Brent sucked in a ragged breath as his body fought a war between two potent forces. Love and desire. If he didn't say something soon he would haul her back into his arms.

Or, worse, tell her he loved her.

He had to distance himself from her, both physically and emotionally. She had to know that what had happened between them in the wee small hours had been an anomaly.

For his own sanity he had to declare his intention of keeping her arm's length.

His old job back at the Royal Melbourne suddenly seemed

very attractive. Working with her when sexual attraction had been the only issue had been difficult but doable. But now love was in the equation he didn't think he could see her every day and not eventually go stark, raving mad.

Then she'd probably get his job here, which was what she'd wanted all along.

It would be win-win.

Except he'd be miserable.

He took a small step back from her and cleared his throat. 'About earlier.'

Grace held her breath. His presence was intoxicating and she wanted to reclaim the step he'd taken away.

But *he* had taken the step away.

Could he be any clearer?

'I'm sorry, that was my fault,' she said quickly. 'I was upset… you were just trying to comfort me. I… Let's just forget it, okay? And you know, it's…this attraction thing…it's probably out of our system now, right? It's probably the purge we were meant to have.'

Brent nodded, even though he knew she would never be out of his system. That he would love her, dream about their on-call tryst, for ever. His hands still stuffed deep in his pockets, he rocked back and forth on the balls of his feet.

'Absolutely. I just wanted to check we're both on the same page.'

'Of course,' she rushed to assure him.

Brent felt her eagerness to be done punch him right in the gut. He had to get away. He couldn't bear being near her, knowing he loved her and she couldn't be his.

'All right. So I'll see you around.'

Grace nodded, just wanting him to go so she could lick her wounds without an audience. Whoever had said that thing about setting love free knew nothing about being a two-time loser in the relationship game.

She watched him turn. Watched his broad shoulders and back retreat, watched his lovely butt sway closer to the door.

And she was stricken with a sudden sense of panic. A feeling that if she let the man that she loved walk out of this room she'd regret it for ever. That if she didn't tell him now, she never would.

She'd told Tash that she couldn't live her life thinking every day was her last. But what if this was *her* last—as Tash had pointed out, no one knew when their time was up.

Would she have regrets?

Damn straight she would.

She'd been so busy telling herself she didn't have time in her life for a man. For another single human being. Making excuses to keep them apart. She'd forgotten what her mother always said.

Love doesn't divide, it multiplies.

Eighteen months ago she'd thought there wasn't room for anyone in her life. But there was. Tash and Benji had fitted right in. Expanded it. Made her better.

How much better would it be with the man she loved?

There *was* room in her life for Brent—her heart was big enough for all of them.

And what kind of a carer would she be to Tash and Benji when so much of her focus would be on losing Brent? She had some tough years ahead and she didn't want to do it alone. Sure, she had her family, but she needed more. Wanted more. She wanted the man she loved by her side, helping her through it all.

But did he love her? Feel anything for her at all? Had she misread the signals the last couple of weeks? And if he did, would he want a part of her insane life?

He was in the doorway when she called out softly, 'Wait.'

Brent stilled, his hands gripped the architrave of the doorframe. His heart was pounding in his chest.

No.

No, no, no.

So close. He was so close to walking away with his secret intact.

Grace took a deep breath. 'I love you.'

Brent stood stock still in the doorway, his back to her, for a few moments.

What?

He was too confused to be elated. Too wary. He turned slowly.

'What did you say?'

Grace almost threw up. His face was so grim, his jaw set so hard she was afraid it was going to shatter.

Oh, God, she'd made a horrible mistake.

But it was out now. And giving voice to those three little words, even knowing there was so many more to come, had lifted an enormous weight.

'I said…I love you.'

She held her hand up quickly, not wanting him to speak until it was all out. Until she'd confessed it all.

'I'm sorry. I know it's not what you want to hear. And I really hadn't planned it. I wasn't going to say anything—truly, I was just going to quietly live with it. But Tash and I have been talking about regrets and I realised as you were walking away that I didn't want you to be my biggest regret.'

Brent shook his head. Had he really heard right? Or had his desperate, love-starved imagination just conjured it up? Was he hallucinating?

Not what he wanted to hear? Was she mad?

'I realised the day of that first footy match but I also knew I'd hurt you too much in the past. That I'd ruined any second chance I had with you. I knew that I'd have to fight for your love and, Brent, I'm sorry, but I'm so over fighting. I've just come out of this battle with Tash…I hope…and I'm too tired to fight with anyone else.'

Brent took a few paces towards her. *She loved him?*

'Grace?'

Grace shook her head. 'No, stop. Don't come any closer. Please. I can't think when you're near me.'

Brent stopped.

'Where was I?'

'You love me,' Brent supplied.

Grace nodded. 'Yes.' She gestured helplessly. 'I'm sorry.'

Brent was silent for a moment then he smiled. The smile turned into a laugh. She loved him and she was sorry? His heart had felt like lead in his chest just moments ago but suddenly it floated as light as air.

She frowned. 'What?'

Brent took a couple more steps towards her. 'Don't be sorry.'

'Why not?' He was smiling and laughing. She was confused, even as a little piece of her heart glowed with hope. 'It's a disaster.'

'No.' He shook his head. 'It would be a disaster if I didn't love you back.'

His words took a moment to sink in and even then she didn't dare hope as she cruelly snuffed out the little flare of light in her chest.

He moved so he was standing right in front of her now. Close. Very close. 'But I do.'

Grace eased the breath out of her lungs. 'You do?'

He nodded. 'I realised just before we made love. It was horrible. I'd spent all these months denying my feelings for you and suddenly it was so clear.'

Grace latched on to the one word she could understand. 'Yes, it is horrible.'

Brent chuckled again. 'No. It's perfect.'

Grace kept the wild leap of her pulse under control. 'But don't you see? It's not as simple as it was twenty years ago, Brent. I come with a lot of added extras. It's never going to be just you and me. And you deserve more than a woman with divided interests. You grew up on crumbs of people's love, you deserve more than that.'

Brent reached for her, put his hands on her waist, hooked his fingers through the loops of her jeans and dragged her hips forward until they were snuggled into his.

'Are you telling me that you're only going to give me crumbs?'

Grace kept her torso erect and as far from his as possible given the closeness of their hips. 'No, of course not.'

God, if she was given the chance she would love this wonderful man with every fibre of her being for all eternity.

'I keep thinking about that thing that Mum always says, you know? That love multiplies. I know I can expand my life to add you into it because I've already done that with the kids. But I think it's a lot to ask you to take on and I know you want kids of your own and I just don't know if that will ever happen. It'll probably just be the four of us. I know you always wanted the perfect family, Brent, and we are far from that. It's not going to be like it was the first time around.'

Brent shook his head. Sometimes this incredibly smart woman could be as dumb as a rock. 'You're my family, Grace. It's always been you. I spent a long time searching for what we had, searching for you in someone else, but I couldn't ever find it. Because it's right here.'

Grace didn't know what to say to that. She felt tears at the back of her eyes and couldn't believe there could actually be any more to shed after the events of the last few hours.

'So what, you guys aren't perfect.' He shrugged. 'I'll take you however you come, Grace. Families come in all shapes and sizes. I know that better than anyone. Of course it's not going to be like it was,' he said, stroking her cheek. 'It's going to be better.'

He slid a hand up her back and urged her towards him but she resisted. She loved him, the mere thought that this might actually work out hummed through her blood. But she had to be sure he knew what he was letting himself in for.

'Better? A teenage girl and a little boy who will also, I should point out, be a teenager before we know it?'

Before *we* know it. Brent knew he'd won then. 'All they need is love, Grace. I can do that. Just let me. Let me love you. Let me love all of you.'

Grace felt his hand at her back, bringing her closer, and she almost gave in to that knowing look in his tawny gaze but still she resisted. 'My whole crazy, in-your-face, in-your-business family?'

'I love your family.'

Grace felt her heart fighting to be let free. 'Benji wants a puppy,' she said.

Brent leaned in and kissed her neck. 'I love puppies.'

Grace's eyes rolled back in her head as Brent's tongue lapped at the pulse fluttering madly in her neck.

She loved him so much. Could this really be true?

'Gracie,' he whispered in her ear. 'I love you. We'll work the rest out as we go along. Just say yes.'

Grace sighed, letting all her reservations fly free as she melted into his arms.

'Yes.'

0611 Gen Std HB

JULY 2011
HARDBACK TITLES

ROMANCE

The Marriage Betrayal	Lynne Graham
The Ice Prince	Sandra Marton
Doukakis's Apprentice	Sarah Morgan
Surrender to the Past	Carole Mortimer
Heart of the Desert	Carol Marinelli
Reckless Night in Rio	Jennie Lucas
Her Impossible Boss	Cathy Williams
The Replacement Wife	Caitlin Crews
Dating and Other Dangers	Natalie Anderson
The S Before Ex	Mira Lyn Kelly
Her Outback Commander	Margaret Way
A Kiss to Seal the Deal	Nikki Logan
Baby on the Ranch	Susan Meier
The Army Ranger's Return	Soraya Lane
Girl in a Vintage Dress	Nicola Marsh
Rapunzel in New York	Nikki Logan
The Doctor & the Runaway Heiress	Marion Lennox
The Surgeon She Never Forgot	Melanie Milburne

HISTORICAL

Seduced by the Scoundrel	Louise Allen
Unmasking the Duke's Mistress	Margaret McPhee
To Catch a Husband…	Sarah Mallory
The Highlander's Redemption	Marguerite Kaye

MEDICAL™

The Playboy of Harley Street	Anne Fraser
Doctor on the Red Carpet	Anne Fraser
Just One Last Night...	Amy Andrews
Suddenly Single Sophie	Leonie Knight

JULY 2011
LARGE PRINT TITLES

ROMANCE

A Stormy Spanish Summer	Penny Jordan
Taming the Last St Claire	Carole Mortimer
Not a Marrying Man	Miranda Lee
The Far Side of Paradise	Robyn Donald
The Baby Swap Miracle	Caroline Anderson
Expecting Royal Twins!	Melissa McClone
To Dance with a Prince	Cara Colter
Molly Cooper's Dream Date	Barbara Hannay

HISTORICAL

Lady Folbroke's Delicious Deception	Christine Merrill
Breaking the Governess's Rules	Michelle Styles
Her Dark and Dangerous Lord	Anne Herries
How To Marry a Rake	Deb Marlowe

MEDICAL™

Sheikh, Children's Doctor...Husband	Meredith Webber
Six-Week Marriage Miracle	Jessica Matthews
Rescued by the Dreamy Doc	Amy Andrews
Navy Officer to Family Man	Emily Forbes
St Piran's: Italian Surgeon, Forbidden Bride	Margaret McDonagh
The Baby Who Stole the Doctor's Heart	Dianne Drake

AUGUST 2011 HARDBACK TITLES

ROMANCE

Bride for Real	Lynne Graham
From Dirt to Diamonds	Julia James
The Thorn in His Side	Kim Lawrence
Fiancée for One Night	Trish Morey
The Untamed Argentinian	Susan Stephens
After the Greek Affair	Chantelle Shaw
The Highest Price to Pay	Maisey Yates
Under the Brazilian Sun	Catherine George
There's Something About a Rebel...	Anne Oliver
The Crown Affair	Lucy King
Australia's Maverick Millionaire	Margaret Way
Rescued by the Brooding Tycoon	Lucy Gordon
Not-So-Perfect Princess	Melissa McClone
The Heart of a Hero	Barbara Wallace
Swept Off Her Stilettos	Fiona Harper
Mr Right There All Along	Jackie Braun
The Tortured Rebel	Alison Roberts
Dating Dr Delicious	Laura Iding

HISTORICAL

Married to a Stranger	Louise Allen
A Dark and Brooding Gentleman	Margaret McPhee
Seducing Miss Lockwood	Helen Dickson
The Highlander's Return	Marguerite Kaye

MEDICAL™

The Doctor's Reason to Stay	Dianne Drake
Career Girl in the Country	Fiona Lowe
Wedding on the Baby Ward	Lucy Clark
Special Care Baby Miracle	Lucy Clark

0711 Gen Std LP

AUGUST 2011
LARGE PRINT TITLES

ROMANCE

Jess's Promise	Lynne Graham
Not For Sale	Sandra Marton
After Their Vows	Michelle Reid
A Spanish Awakening	Kim Lawrence
In the Australian Billionaire's Arms	Margaret Way
Abby and the Bachelor Cop	Marion Lennox
Misty and the Single Dad	Marion Lennox
Daycare Mum to Wife	Jennie Adams

HISTORICAL

Miss in a Man's World	Anne Ashley
Captain Corcoran's Hoyden Bride	Annie Burrows
His Counterfeit Condesa	Joanna Fulford
Rebellious Rake, Innocent Governess	Elizabeth Beacon

MEDICAL™

Cedar Bluff's Most Eligible Bachelor	Laura Iding
Doctor: Diamond in the Rough	Lucy Clark
Becoming Dr Bellini's Bride	Joanna Neil
Midwife, Mother...Italian's Wife	Fiona McArthur
St Piran's: Daredevil, Doctor...Dad!	Anne Fraser
Single Dad's Triple Trouble	Fiona Lowe

CAP